Excel

YEARS 9 to 11

Step-by-Step Algebra 3 Workbook

ESSENTIAL skills

Get the Results You Want!

PASCAL PRESS

Lyn Baker

ISBN 978 1 74020 042 4

Pascal Press
PO Box 250
Glebe NSW 2037
(02) 8585 4044
www.pascalpress.com.au

Publisher: Vivienne Joannou
Edited by Ken Tate
Typeset by Big Picture Communications and Grizzly Graphics (Leanne Richters)
Cover by Dizign Pty Ltd
Printed by Vivar Printing/Green Giant Press

MIX
Paper from
responsible sources
FSC® C084469

TABLE OF CONTENTS

INTRODUCTION

This book is the third in a series of three on algebra and builds on the knowledge gained from the first and second books. A review of the important basic concepts has been included. While it would be an advantage to have worked through the previous books, students with a sound knowledge of basic algebra should be able to understand and benefit from this book. Having completed and understood the concepts in this book, students should have a good grasp of algebra and should be well prepared to tackle further studies in maths.

Each section is devoted to one aspect of the course and consists of four pages. The first page explains the content and gives plenty of examples which should be carefully read and understood. This is followed by a question page which should be completed, using the examples as a guide. After the questions, the next two pages provide fully worked solutions to every question, with further explanations and hints.

At the end of the book is a glossary of common words used in algebra and their meanings.

> Like terms have exactly the same pronumeral part.
> Only like terms can be added and subtracted.
> Unlike terms cannot be simplified.

Example:

(a) $7k^2 - 4k + k^2$ (b) $3m - 2n + 8m - 5n$ (c) $9t^3 - 3t^2 + 5t^2 + 2 + 4t^3$

Solution:

(a) $7k^2 - 4k + k^2 = \mathbf{8k^2 - 4k}$ (b) $3m - 2n + 8m - 5n = \mathbf{11m - 7n}$ (c) $9t^3 - 3t^2 + 5t^2 + 2 + 4t^3 = \mathbf{13t^3 + 2t^2 + 2}$

> When multiplying, if the base is the same, add the indices. $a^m \times a^n = a^{m+n}$
> When dividing, if the base is the same, subtract the indices. $a^m \div a^n = a^{m-n}$
> When raising a power to a power, multiply the indices. $(a^m)^n = a^{mn}$

Example:

(a) $9x^2y \times 3xy$ (b) $(3a^4b^2)^3$ (c) $12p^5q \div 4p^2 + 3p^2 \times 5q$ (d) $32n^7 \div 2(n^3)^2$

Solution:

(a) $9x^2y \times 3xy = \mathbf{27x^3y^2}$ (b) $(3a^4b^2)^3 = \mathbf{27a^{12}b^6}$

(c) $12p^5q \div 4p^2 + 3p^2 \times 5q = \mathbf{3p^3q + 15p^2q}$ (d) $32n^7 \div 2(n^3)^2 = \mathbf{32n^7 \div 2n^6}$
$$= \mathbf{16n}$$

> When expanding grouping symbols, every term inside the bracket must be multiplied by the term outside.

Example:

(a) $7(3x - 8y)$ (b) $-4(1 - 4e^3)$ (c) $3x^2y(x^3 + 2xy)$ (d) $-(x - y + z)$

Solution:

(a) $7(3x - 8y) = \mathbf{21x - 56y}$ (b) $-4(1 - 4e^3) = \mathbf{-4 + 16e^3}$

(c) $3x^2y(x^3 + 2xy) = \mathbf{3x^5y + 6x^3y^2}$ (d) $-(x - y + z) = \mathbf{-x + y - z}$

> Don't forget!
> We must take extra care with the operation signs when subtracting terms in brackets.

Example:

(a) $6(3x - 2y) + 5(x - y)$ (b) $12 - 4(3 - 5a)$ (c) $x(x + 5) - 8(x + 5)$ (d) $3a(2a - 5b) - (5a - 2b)$

Solution:

(a) $6(3x - 2y) + 5(x - y) = \mathbf{18x - 12y + 5x - 5y}$ (b) $12 - 4(3 - 5a) = \mathbf{12 - 12 + 20a}$
$$= \mathbf{23x - 17y} \qquad\qquad = \mathbf{20a}$$

(c) $x(x + 5) - 8(x + 5) = \mathbf{x^2 + 5x - 8x - 40}$ (d) $3a(2a - 5b) - (5a - 2b) = \mathbf{6a^2 - 15ab - 5a + 2b}$
$$= \mathbf{x^2 - 3x - 40}$$

1. **Find:**

   (a) $6x^2 + 5x + 4x^2 + 3x$ = _____

   (b) $9k - 8 + k - 7$ = _____

   (c) $4a + 6b - a - 7b$ = _____

   (d) $2d^2 + 3d^2 + 5d + 8$ = _____

   (e) $-6p + 4q - 7q + 3p + p$ = _____

   (f) $5g^3 + 2g^2 - 3g^2 + 5g^3 - 2$ = _____

   (g) $6t - 4t^2 - 8t^2$ = _____

   (h) $7x - 8z + 9 - 3y$ = _____

   (i) $5m - 2n + 7 - 3m + n - 11$ = _____

   (j) $-3b^2 + 4b - 1 - 5b^2 - 4b + 1$ = _____

2. **Find:**

   (a) $3p^4 \times 2p^5$ = _____

   (b) $9h^9 \div 3h^3$ = _____

   (c) $7x^2y^3 \times 3xy^2$ = _____

   (d) $a^5b^6 \times a^3b^4$ = _____

   (e) $5e^3 \times 2e^5 \times 7e$ = _____

   (f) $6c^8d^6 \div 3c^4d$ = _____

   (g) $(4a^2)^3$ = _____

   (h) $5(n^5)^4$ = _____

   (i) $(2p^6q^2)^2$ = _____

   (j) $3k^5 \times 4k^3 + 2k^6 \times 5k^2$ = _____

   = _____

   (k) $9g^6 \div 3g^4 - 12g^7 \div 4g^5$ = _____

   = _____

   (l) $(3x^2)^3 + 5x \times 3x$ = _____

   = _____

   (m) $(2a^4b^2)^3 \times (3a^3b)^2$ = _____

   = _____

3. **Expand:**

   (a) $6(2a + 5b)$ = _____

   (b) $7(4x - 9)$ = _____

   (c) $-3(t - 2)$ = _____

   (d) $-5(5e + 1)$ = _____

   (e) $x(x - 7)$ = _____

   (f) $4m(2m + 3)$ = _____

   (g) $-(3 - y)$ = _____

   (h) $-(5g + 4h)$ = _____

   (i) $-2x(x - 1)$ = _____

   (j) $-4(3p + 2q - r)$ = _____

   (k) $2xy(xy + 3x - 2y)$ = _____

   (l) $3a^2(a - 2)$ = _____

   (m) $4a^2b^3(a^2 - b)$ = _____

4. **Expand and simplify:**

   (a) $4(2c + 5) + 3(c - 3)$

   (b) $2(7a - 3b) + 3(a - 2b)$

   (c) $5(x - y) - 4(x + y)$

   (d) $7(4y - 1) - 5(1 - y)$

   (e) $x(x + 4) - 3(x - 4)$

   (f) $3p(2p - 5q) - (7p - q)$

1. Find:

(a) $6x^2 + 5x + 4x^2 + 3x = \mathbf{10x^2 + 8x}$ ☞ Collecting like terms, $6x^2 + 4x^2 = 10x^2$, $5x + 3x = 8x$

(b) $9k - 8 + k - 7 = \mathbf{10k - 15}$ ☞ $9k + k = 10k$, $-8 - 7 = -15$

(c) $4a + 6b - a - 7b = \mathbf{3a - b}$

(d) $2d^2 + 3d^2 + 5d + 8 = \mathbf{5d^2 + 5d + 8}$

(e) $-6p + 4q - 7q + 3p + p = \mathbf{-2p - 3q}$

(f) $5g^3 + 2g^2 - 3g^2 + 5g^3 - 2 = \mathbf{10g^3 - g^2 - 2}$

(g) $6t - 4t^2 - 8t^2 = \mathbf{6t - 12t^2}$ ☞ $-12t^2 + 6t$ is the same thing.

(h) $7x - 8z + 9 - 3y = \mathbf{7x - 8z + 9 - 3y}$ ☞ These are unlike terms so cannot be simplified.

(i) $5m - 2n + 7 - 3m + n - 11 = \mathbf{2m - n - 4}$

(j) $-3b^2 + 4b - 1 - 5b^2 - 4b + 1 = \mathbf{-8b^2}$ ☞ On collecting like terms.

2. Find:

(a) $3p^4 \times 2p^5 = \mathbf{6p^9}$ ☞ Multiply the numbers; add the indices.

(b) $9h^9 \div 3h^3 = \mathbf{3h^6}$ ☞ Divide the numbers; subtract the indices.

(c) $7x^2y^3 \times 3xy^2 = \mathbf{21x^3y^5}$ ☞ Add the indices separately for each pronumeral; x^{2+1}, y^{3+2}.

(d) $a^5b^6 \times a^3b^4 = \mathbf{a^8b^{10}}$

(e) $5e^3 \times 2e^5 \times 7e = \mathbf{70e^9}$

(f) $6c^8d^6 \div 3c^4d = \mathbf{2c^4d^5}$

(g) $(4a^2)^3 = \mathbf{64a^6}$ ☞ $4^3 = 64$; multiply the indices.

(h) $5(n^5)^4 = \mathbf{5n^{20}}$ ☞ 5 is not in the brackets, so is not raised to the power.

(i) $(2p^6q^2)^2 = \mathbf{4p^{12}q^4}$ ☞ $2^2 = 4$; multiply the indices, separately.

(j) $3k^5 \times 4k^3 + 2k^6 \times 5k^2 = \mathbf{12k^8 + 10k^8}$ ☞ Multiplication is done before addition. Collect like terms.
$= \mathbf{22k^8}$

(k) $9g^6 \div 3g^4 - 12g^7 \div 4g^5 = \mathbf{3g^2 - 3g^2}$ ☞ Division is done before subtraction. Collect like terms.
$= \mathbf{0}$

(l) $(3x^2)^3 + 5x \times 3x = \mathbf{27x^6 + 15x^2}$ ☞ First remove brackets, then multiply. Unlike terms cannot be simplified.

(m) $(2a^4b^2)^3 \times (3a^3b)^2 = \mathbf{8a^{12}b^6 \times 9a^6b^2}$ ☞ First remove grouping symbols; then multiply.
$= \mathbf{72a^{18}b^8}$

3. Expand:

(a) $6(2a + 5b) = \mathbf{12a + 30b}$ ☞ $6 \times 2a + 6 \times 5b$

(b) $7(4x - 9) = \mathbf{28x - 63}$ ☞ $7 \times 4x - 7 \times 9$

(c) $-3(t - 2) = \mathbf{-3t + 6}$ ☞ $-3t - (-6) = -3t + 6$
Be careful with the signs.

(d) $-5(5e + 1) = \mathbf{-25e - 5}$

(e) $x(x - 7) = \mathbf{x^2 - 7x}$ ☞ $x \times x - x \times 7$

(f) $4m(2m + 3) = \mathbf{8m^2 + 12m}$

(g) $-(3 - y) = \mathbf{-3 + y}$ ☞ $-(3 - y)$ means $-1(3 - y)$.
Be careful with the signs.

(h) $-(5g + 4h) = \mathbf{-5g - 4h}$

(i) $-2x(x - 1) = \mathbf{-2x^2 + 2x}$

(j) $-4(3p + 2q - r) = \mathbf{-12p - 8q + 4r}$

(k) $2xy(xy + 3x - 2y) = \mathbf{2x^2y^2 + 6x^2y - 4xy^2}$

(l) $3a^2(a - 2) = \mathbf{3a^3 - 6a^2}$

(m) $4a^2b^3(a^2 - b) = \mathbf{4a^4b^3 - 4a^2b^4}$

4. Expand and simplify:

(a) $4(2c + 5) + 3(c - 3) = \mathbf{8c + 20 + 3c - 9}$ ☞ $4 \times 2c + 4 \times 5 + 3 \times c - 3 \times 3$
$= \mathbf{11c + 11}$ Collecting like terms.

(b) $2(7a - 3b) + 3(a - 2b) = \mathbf{14a - 6b + 3a - 6b}$
$= \mathbf{17a - 12b}$

(c) $5(x - y) - 4(x + y) = \mathbf{5x - 5y - 4x - 4y}$ ☞ Be careful with the signs.
$= \mathbf{x - 9y}$

(d) $7(4y - 1) - 5(1 - y) = \mathbf{28y - 7 - 5 + 5y}$ ☞ Be careful with the signs.
$= \mathbf{33y - 12}$

(e) $x(x + 4) - 3(x - 4) = \mathbf{x^2 + 4x - 3x + 12}$
$= \mathbf{x^2 + x + 12}$

(f) $3p(2p - 5q) - (7p - q) = \mathbf{6p^2 - 15pq - 7p + q}$ ☞ $-(7p - q)$ means $-1(7p - q)$.
Unlike terms cannot be simplified.

$$(a + b)(x + y) = a(x + y) + b(x + y)$$
$$= ax + ay + bx + by$$
Each term in the second brackets must be multiplied
by each term in the first brackets.

Example:
Expand: (a) $(x + 2)(y + 3)$ (b) $(a + 4)(a - 7)$ (c) $(2t - 3)(t + 7)$ (d) $(4x - 3y)(2y + 3z)$

Solution:

(a) $(x + 2)(y + 3) = xy + 3x + 2y + 6$

(b) $(a + 4)(a - 7) = a^2 - 7a + 4a - 28$
$$= a^2 - 3a - 28$$

(c) $(2t - 3)(t + 7) = 2t^2 + 14t - 3t - 21$
$$= 2t^2 + 11t - 21$$

(d) $(4x - 3y)(2y + 3z) = 8xy + 12xz - 6y^2 - 9yz$

When we multiply the **sum** of two terms **by** their **difference** we get a special binomial product:
$$(x + y)(x - y) = x^2 - y^2$$
The answer is always the difference of two squares.

Example:
Find: (a) $(t + 7)(t - 7)$ (b) $(3k - 4)(3k + 4)$ (c) $(2y + 9z)(2y - 9z)$ (d) $(m^2 - 1)(m^2 + 1)$

Solution:

(a) $(t + 7)(t - 7) = t^2 - 7^2$
$$= t^2 - 49$$

(b) $(3k - 4)(3k + 4) = (3k)^2 - 4^2$
$$= 9k^2 - 16$$

(c) $(2y + 9z)(2y - 9z) = (2y)^2 - (9z)^2$
$$= 4y^2 - 81z^2$$

(d) $(m^2 - 1)(m^2 + 1) = (m^2)^2 - 1^2$
$$= m^4 - 1$$

The square of a binomial
$$(x + a)^2 = x^2 + 2ax + a^2 \qquad (x - a)^2 = x^2 - 2ax + a^2$$

Example:
Find: (a) $(g - 4)^2$ (b) $(2t + 3)^2$ (c) $(9p - 7q)^2$ (d) $(2a^2 + 5bc)^2$

Solution:

(a) $(g - 4)^2 = g^2 - 2 \times g \times 4 + 4^2$
$$= g^2 - 8g + 16$$

(b) $(2t + 3)^2 = (2t)^2 + 2 \times 2t \times 3 + 3^2$
$$= 4t^2 + 12t + 9$$

(c) $(9p - 7q)^2 = (9p)^2 - 2 \times 9p \times 7q + (7q)^2$
$$= 81p^2 - 126pq + 49q^2$$

(d) $(2a^2 + 5bc)^2 = (2a^2)^2 + 2 \times 2a^2 \times 5bc + (5bc)^2$
$$= 4a^4 + 20a^2bc + 25b^2c^2$$

We can add and subtract any combination of these products.

Example:
Find: (a) $(m - 2)(m + 1) - (m - 1)^2$ (b) $(5k - 2)(5k + 2) - (1 - k)(1 + k)$

Solution:

(a) $(m - 2)(m + 1) - (m - 1)^2$
$$= (m^2 + m - 2m - 2) - (m^2 - 2 \times m \times 1 + 1^2)$$
$$= (m^2 - m - 2) - (m^2 - 2m + 1)$$
$$= m^2 - m - 2 - m^2 + 2m - 1$$
$$= m - 3$$

(b) $(5k - 2)(5k + 2) - (1 - k)(1 + k)$
$$= ((5k)^2 - 2^2) - (1^2 - k^2)$$
$$= (25k^2 - 4) - (1 - k^2)$$
$$= 25k^2 - 4 - 1 + k^2$$
$$= 26k^2 - 5$$

1. **Expand:**

    (a) $(x + 4)(x + 7)$ = _____

    = _____

    (b) $(a + 3)(a - 5)$ = _____

    = _____

    (c) $(e - f)(e + g)$ = _____

    = _____

    (d) $(2g + 5)(3g - 8)$ = _____

    = _____

    (e) $(5k - 1)(k + 2)$ = _____

    = _____

    (f) $(3y - 2z)(2y - 9z)$ = _____

    = _____

2. **Find:**

    (a) $(e + 4)(e - 4)$ = _____

    = _____

    (b) $(t + 1)(t - 1)$ = = _____

    = _____

    (c) $(8p + 3q)(8p - 3q)$ = _____

    = _____

    (d) $(5 - 2n)(5 + 2n)$ = _____

    = _____

    (e) $(7m - n)(7m + n)$ = _____

    = _____

    (f) $(a^2 + b^2)(a^2 - b^2)$ = _____

    = _____

3. **Find:**

    (a) $(m + 7)^2$ = _____

    = _____

    (b) $(e - 3)^2$ = _____

    = _____

    (c) $(5t - 4)^2$ = _____

    = _____

    (d) $(1 - 9h)^2$ = _____

    = _____

    (e) $(ab - c)^2$ = _____

    = _____

    (f) $(n^2 + 2)^2$ = _____

    = _____

4. **Find:**

    (a) $(5t - 2u)(t + 2u)$ = _____

    = _____

    (b) $(11 - 2b)(11 + 2b)$ = _____

    = _____

    (c) $(6x + 5y)^2$ = _____

    = _____

    (d) $(9 + 2z)(4z - 9)$ = _____

    = _____

    (e) $(7q - 6)^2$ = _____

    = _____

    (f) $(4k + 7)(4k - 7)$ = _____

    = _____

5. **Expand and simplify:**

    (a) $(3m + n)^2 + (2m + 3n)(2m - 3n)$

    = _____

    = _____

    = _____

    (b) $(2e + 7)(2e - 7) - (e - 2)^2$

    = _____

    = _____

    = _____

1 Expand:

   (a) $(x+4)(x+7) = x^2 + 7x + 4x + 28$ ☞ Each term in the second brackets must be multiplied by each term in the first brackets.

                   $= x^2 + 11x + 28$

   (b) $(a+3)(a-5) = a^2 - 5a + 3a - 15$ ☞ $a(a-5) + 3(a-5)$

                   $= a^2 - 2a - 15$

   (c) $(e-f)(e+g) = e^2 + eg - ef - fg$ ☞ These are unlike terms and cannot be simplified. *fe* is the same as *ef*, but when we use letters as pronumerals we usually write them in alphabetical order.

   (d) $(2g+5)(3g-8) = 6g^2 - 16g + 15g - 40$

                   $= 6g^2 - g - 40$ ☞ Collecting like terms.

   (e) $(5k-1)(k+2) = 5k^2 + 10k - k - 2$ ☞ Be careful with the signs.

                   $= 5k^2 + 9k - 2$

   (f) $(3y-2z)(2y-9z) = 6y^2 - 27yz - 4yz + 18z^2$ ☞ $4zy$ is the same thing as $4yz$.

                   $= 6y^2 - 31yz + 18z^2$

2. Find:

   (a) $(e+4)(e-4) = e^2 - 4^2$ ☞ This is a sum by difference.

               $= e^2 - 16$

   (b) $(t+1)(t-1) = t^2 - 1^2$

               $= t^2 - 1$

   (c) $(8p+3q)(8p-3q) = (8p)^2 - (3q)^2$

                       $= 64p^2 - 9q^2$ ☞ Every part of each term must be squared.

   (d) $(5-2n)(5+2n) = 5^2 - (2n)^2$

                   $= 25 - 4n^2$

   (e) $(7m-n)(7m+n) = (7m)^2 - n^2$

                   $= 49m^2 - n^2$

   (f) $(a^2+b^2)(a^2-b^2) = (a^2)^2 - (b^2)^2$

                   $= a^4 - b^4$ ☞ Multiply the indices.

3. Find:

   (a) $(m+7)^2 = m^2 + 2 \times m \times 7 + 7^2$ ☞ Using the rule $(x+y)^2 = x^2 + 2xy + y^2$

             $= m^2 + 14m + 49$

   (b) $(e-3)^2 = e^2 - 2 \times e \times 3 + 3^2$ ☞ Using the rule $(x-y)^2 = x^2 - 2xy + y^2$

             $= e^2 - 6e + 9$ Make sure the signs are correct.

(c) $(5t - 4)^2 = (5t)^2 - 2 \times 5t \times 4 + 4^2$
  $= 25t^2 - 40t + 16$ ☞ $(5t)^2 = 25t^2$. The 5 must be squared.

(d) $(1 - 9h)^2 = 1^2 - 2 \times 1 \times 9h + (9h)^2$
  $= 1 - 18h + 81h^2$

(e) $(ab - c)^2 = (ab)^2 - 2 \times ab \times c + c^2$
  $= a^2b^2 - 2abc + c^2$ ☞ $(ab)^2 - 2abc + c^2$ is the same thing.

(f) $(n^2 + 2)^2 = (n^2)^2 + 2 \times n^2 \times 2 + 2^2$
  $= n^4 + 4n^2 + 4$

4. Find:

(a) $(5t - 2u)(t + 2u) = 5t^2 + 10tu - 2tu - 4u^2$ ☞ Binomial product.
  $= 5t^2 + 8tu - 4u^2$ ☞ $2ut$ is the same thing as $2tu$.

(b) $(11 - 2b)(11 + 2b) = 11^2 - (2b)^2$ ☞ Sum by difference.
  $= 121 - 4b^2$

(c) $(6x + 5y)^2 = (6x)^2 + 2 \times 6x \times 5y + (5y)^2$ ☞ Perfect square.
  $= 36x^2 + 60xy + 25y^2$

(d) $(9 + 2z)(4z - 9) = 36z - 81 + 8z^2 - 18z$ ☞ Binomial product.
  $= 18z - 81 + 8z^2$ $8z^2 + 18z - 81$ is the same thing.

(e) $(7q - 6)^2 = (7q)^2 - 2 \times 7q \times 6 + 6^2$ ☞ Perfect square.
  $= 49q^2 - 84q + 36$

(f) $(4k + 7)(4k - 7) = (4k)^2 - 7^2$ ☞ Sum by difference.
  $= 16k^2 - 49$

5. Expand and simplify:

(a) $(3m + n)^2 + (2m + 3n)(2m - 3n)$
  $= ((3m)^2 + 2 \times 3m \times n + n^2) + ((2m)^2 - (3n)^2)$
  $= 9m^2 + 6mn + n^2 + 4m^2 - 9n^2$
  $= 13m^2 + 6mn - 8n^2$ ☞ On collecting like terms.
    $13m^2 - 8n^2 + 6mn$ is the same thing.

(b) $(2e + 7)(2e - 7) - (e - 2)^2$ ☞ All of $(e - 2)^2$ must be subtracted.
  $= ((2e)^2 - 7^2) - (e^2 - 2 \times e \times 2 + 2^2)$ Use brackets.
  $= (4e^2 - 49) - (e^2 - 4e + 4)$
  $= 4e^2 - 49 - e^2 + 4e - 4$
  $= 3e^2 + 4e - 53$

Equations can be solved by:
- adding the same number to both sides of the equation;
- subtracting the same number from both sides of the equation;
- multiplying both sides of the equation by the same number;
- dividing both sides of the equation by the same number.

Example:

Solve: (a) $\frac{n}{8} + 5 = 12$ (b) $9k - 15 = 36 - 6k$

Solution:

(a) $\frac{n}{8} + 5 = 12$

$\frac{n}{8} = 7$ [subtracting 5]

$n = 56$ [multiplying by 8]

(b) $9k - 15 = 36 - 6k$

$9k = 51 - 6k$ [adding 15]

$15k = 51$ [adding $6k$]

$k = 3.4$ [dividing by 15]

We must remove any grouping symbols and collect any like terms before solving the equation.

Example:
Solve: (a) $7(2x + 5) - 2(3x - 1) = 17$ (b) $6(4p - 1) - 5(p + 4) = 7(3p - 2)$

Solution:

(a) $7(2x + 5) - 2(3x - 1) = 17$

$14x + 35 - 6x + 2 = 17$

$8x + 37 = 17$

$8x = -20$

$x = -2.5$ [or $x = -2\frac{1}{2}$]

(b) $6(4p - 1) - 5(p + 4) = 7(3p - 2)$

$24p - 6 - 5p - 20 = 21p - 14$

$19p - 26 = 21p - 14$

$-2p - 26 = -14$

$-2p = 12$

$p = -6$

Equations involving fractions can be simplified by multiplying by the common denominator.
Don't forget to multiply every term.
{Use brackets so that every part of each term is multiplied.}

Example:

(a) $\frac{5z - 1}{9} = \frac{2z + 7}{3}$ (b) $\frac{2t}{7} - 5 = \frac{t + 3}{4}$

Solution:

(a) $\frac{5z - 1}{9} = \frac{2z + 7}{3}$

${}^1 9 \times \frac{(5z - 1)}{{}_1 9} = {}^3 9 \times \frac{(2z + 7)}{{}_1 3}$

$5z - 1 = 3(2z + 7)$

$5z - 1 = 6z + 21$

$-z = 22$

$z = -22$ [dividing by -1]

(b) $\frac{2t}{7} - 5 = \frac{t + 3}{4}$

${}^4 28 \times \frac{2t}{{}_1 7} - 28 \times 5 = {}^7 28 \times \frac{(t + 3)}{{}_1 4}$

$8t - 140 = 7(t + 3)$

$8t - 140 = 7t + 21$

$8t = 7t + 161$

$t = 161$

Remember: $-z$ means $-1z$ so, to solve $-z = 22$, we must divide both sides by -1.

1. **Solve:**

   (a) $3a + 17 = 59$

   (b) $6e - 13 = -4$

   (c) $5 - 9x = 68$

   (d) $8k = 3k + 95$

   (e) $\frac{a}{6} + 19 = 37$

   (f) $\frac{d}{7} - 21 = -2$

   (g) $6t - 13 = 4t + 57$

   (h) $8y + 15 = 5 - 2y$

   (i) $7(4p - 9) = 3(p - 11)$

2. **Solve:**

   (a) $7(3k + 2) - 4(5k - 1) = 19$

   (b) $2(5e + 2) + 3(2e - 9) = 5(8e - 7)$

3. **Solve:**

   (a) $\frac{3m}{4} = \frac{m + 6}{2}$

   (b) $\frac{5h + 1}{3} = \frac{3h - 1}{5}$

   (c) $\frac{2n}{3} + 5 = \frac{n + 2}{4}$

   (d) $\frac{m + 3}{7} + \frac{m - 4}{9} = 1$

   (e) $\frac{2y + 3}{5} + y - 4 = \frac{3y - 7}{2}$

1. Solve:

(a) $3a + 17 = 59$
$$3a = 42$$
$$a = 14$$

☞ Subtracting 17 from both sides of the equation.
Dividing both sides of the equation by 3.

(b) $6e - 13 = -4$
$$6e = 9$$
$$e = 1.5$$

☞ Adding 13 to both sides of the equation.
Dividing both sides of the equation by 6.
$e = 1\frac{1}{2}$ is the same thing.

(c) $5 - 9x = 68$
$$-9x = 63$$
$$x = -7$$

☞ Subtracting 5 from both sides of the equation.
Dividing both sides of the equation by -9.

(d) $8k = 3k + 95$
$$5k = 95$$
$$k = 19$$

☞ Subtract $3k$ from both sides of the equation.
Divide both sides by 5.

(e) $\frac{a}{6} + 19 = 37$
$$\frac{a}{6} = 18$$
$$a = 108$$

☞ Subtracting 19 from both sides of the equation.
Multiplying both sides of the equation by 6.

(f) $\frac{d}{7} - 21 = -2$
$$\frac{d}{7} = 19$$
$$d = 133$$

☞ Adding 21 to both sides.
Multiplying both sides by 7.

(g) $6t - 13 = 4t + 57$
$$6t = 4t + 70$$
$$2t = 70$$
$$t = 35$$

☞ Adding 13 to both sides.
Subtracting $4t$ from both sides.
(We could have added 13 and subtracted $4t$ in the same step.)

(h) $8y + 15 = 5 - 2y$
$$8y + 2y = 5 - 15$$
$$10y = -10$$
$$y = -1$$

☞ Add $2y$ to both sides and subtract 15 from both sides.
Those two steps could be done separately.
Dividing both sides by 10.

(i) $7(4p - 9) = 3(p - 11)$
$$28p - 63 = 3p - 33$$
$$28p = 3p + 30$$
$$25p = 30$$
$$p = 1.2$$

☞ First remove grouping symbols;
adding 63 to both sides;
subtracting $3p$ from both sides,
dividing both sides by 25. ($p = 1\frac{1}{5}$ is the same thing.)

2. Solve:

(a) $7(3k + 2) - 4(5k - 1) = 19$
$$21k + 14 - 20k + 4 = 19$$
$$k + 18 = 19$$
$$k = 1$$

☞ First remove brackets, being careful with the signs,
then collect like terms.
Subtracting 18 from both sides of the equation.

(b) $2(5e + 2) + 3(2e - 9) = 5(8e - 7)$

$$10e + 4 + 6e - 27 = 40e - 35$$ ☞ Remove grouping symbols.
$$16e - 23 = 40e - 35$$ Collect like terms.
$$16e = 40e - 12$$ Adding 23 to both sides of the equation.
$$-24e = -12$$ Subtracting 40e from both sides.
$$e = 0.5$$ Dividing both sides by –24. ($e = \frac{1}{2}$ is the same thing.)

3. Solve:

(a) $$\frac{3m}{4} = \frac{m + 6}{2}$$

$$4^1 \times \left(\frac{3m}{4_1}\right) = 4^2 \times \left(\frac{m + 6}{2_1}\right)$$ ☞ Multiplying both sides by 4, the lowest common denominator.

$$3m = 2(m + 6)$$
$$3m = 2m + 12$$
$$m = 12$$ ☞ Subtracting 2m from both sides of the equation.

(b) $$\frac{5h + 1}{3} = \frac{3h - 1}{5}$$

$$15^5 \times \left(\frac{5h + 1}{3_1}\right) = 15^3 \times \left(\frac{3h - 1}{5_1}\right)$$ ☞ Multiplying both sides by the common denominator.

$$5(5h + 1) = 3(3h - 1)$$
$$25h + 5 = 9h - 3$$ ☞ Removing grouping symbols.
$$25h = 9h - 8$$ Subtracting 5 from both sides.
$$16h = -8$$ Subtracting 9h from both sides.
$$h = -\frac{1}{2}$$ Dividing both sides by 16.

(c) $$\frac{2n}{3} + 5 = \frac{n + 2}{4}$$

$$12^4 \times \frac{2n}{3_1} + 12 \times 5 = 12^3 \times \left(\frac{n + 2}{4_1}\right)$$ ☞ Multiply every term by the common denominator.

$$8n + 60 = 3(n + 2)$$
$$8n + 60 = 3n + 6$$
$$5n = -54$$
$$n = -10.8$$ ☞ or $n = -10\frac{4}{5}$

(d) $$\frac{m + 3}{7} + \frac{m - 4}{9} = 1$$

$$63^9 \times \left(\frac{m + 3}{7_1}\right) + 63^7 \times \left(\frac{m - 4}{9_1}\right) = 63 \times 1$$

$$9(m + 3) + 7(m - 4) = 63$$
$$9m + 27 + 7m - 28 = 63$$
$$16m - 1 = 63$$
$$16m = 64$$
$$m = 4$$

(e) $$\frac{2y + 3}{5} + y - 4 = \frac{3y - 7}{2}$$

$$10^2 \times \left(\frac{2y + 3}{5_1}\right) + 10 \times (y - 4) = 10^5 \times \left(\frac{3y - 7}{2_1}\right)$$

$$2(2y + 3) + 10(y - 4) = 5(3y - 7)$$
$$4y + 6 + 10y - 40 = 15y - 35$$
$$14y - 34 = 15y - 35$$
$$-y = -1$$
$$y = 1$$

GENERALISED ARITHMETIC Summary

We can use algebra to solve problems and do calculations even when we do not know the value of any pronumerals.

Example:
If x litres of oil cost y dollars, what would z litres of the same oil cost?

Solution:
x litres of oil cost y dollars

1 litre of oil would cost $\frac{y}{x}$ dollars   (Dividing by x gives the cost of 1 litre)

z litres of oil would cost $\frac{y}{x} \times z$ dollars   (Multiplying by z gives the cost of z litres)

$$= \$\frac{yz}{x}$$

We can find a general expression in many situations.

Example:
A woman leaves home at g pm and returns at h am the next day.
How many hours was she away from home?

Solution:
The woman is out from g pm until midnight the first day. This is $(12 - g)$ hours.
She is out from midnight until h am the next day. This is h hours.
She is away from home for $(12 - g + h)$ hours.

We can use numbers as examples to help us see the pattern.
e.g. If the woman went out at 9 pm and returned at 1 am she was away for 4 hours; 3 to midnight plus 1.
If she went out at 5 pm and returned at 10 am, she was out for 17 hours, 7 to midnight $(12 - 5)$ plus 10.
But we can't use just one example. We must be certain that the pattern will always work.

Example:
If p and q are both negative numbers, determine, if possible, whether the following are positive or negative: (a) $p + q$ (b) $q - p$ (c) pq (d) q^2 (e) $p^2 q$

Solution:
(a) $p + q$ will always be negative   (Try adding any two negative numbers)
(b) $q - p$ will be positive if $p > q$, but negative if $p < q$
(c) pq will always be positive   (A negative multiplied by a negative is always positive)
(d) q^2 will always be positive   (The square of every number, except 0, is positive)
(e) $p^2 q$ will always be negative   (p^2 will be positive, a positive $\times$ negative = negative)

We can also use our rules for expanding or factorising to find general expressions.

Example:
If m and n are consecutive numbers, with $m > n$, find an expression for:
(a) m in terms of n   **(b) $m^2 - n^2$**

Solution:
(a) $m = n + 1$
(b) $m^2 - n^2 = (n + 1)^2 - n^2$
$\qquad\qquad = n^2 + 2n + 1 - n^2$
$\qquad\qquad = 2n + 1$

Remember: Consecutive numbers are numbers that follow one another in order, like 7, 8 and 9

1. If stamps cost h cents each:
   (a) what is the cost of 7 stamps? _____
   (b) what is the cost of n stamps? _____
   (c) what is the change from \$10.00 if you buy b stamps? _____

2. g tiles weigh m kilograms.
   What would be the weight of: (a) 1 tile? _____ (b) k tiles? _____

3. If a carton holds e eggs:
   (a) how many eggs will fit in c cartons? _____
   (b) how many cartons will be needed for j eggs? _____

4. If a car travels at k kilometres per hour:
   (a) how far will it travel in 6 hours? _____
   (b) how far will it travel in w hours? _____
   (c) how long will it take to travel n kilometres? _____
   (d) If it still has p kilometres to travel after travelling for h hours, how long is the trip? _____

5. A television program begins at b am and finishes at c pm the same day.
   How long does the television program run? _____

6. If m and n are two different positive numbers, determine, if possible, whether the following are positive or negative:
   (a) $m + n$ _____ (b) $m - n$ _____
   (c) mn _____ (d) $\frac{n}{m}$ _____
   (e) m^2 _____ (f) $\frac{n^2}{m}$ _____

7. If p, q and r are consecutive numbers, with $p > q > r$, write an expression for:
   (a) q in terms of p _____ (b) r in terms of p _____
   (c) $q^2 - pr$ _____

8. Find a simple expression for:
   (a) the perimeter, and
   (b) the area of this rectangle. (Measurements are in metres.)
   (a) Perimeter =
   (b) Area =

1. If stamps cost h cents each:

    (a) what is the cost of 7 stamps? **7h cents** .... ☞ To find the cost of 7 stamps we multiply the cost of one stamp by 7.

    (b) what is the cost of n stamps? **hn cents** .... ☞ To find the cost of n stamps we multiply the cost of one stamp by n.

    nh cents is the same thing. We usually write letters that are used as pronumerals in alphabetical order.

    (c) what is the change from $10.00
    if you buy b stamps? **(1000 − bh) cents** .... ☞ The cost of b stamps is bh cents.
    $10.00 = 1000 cents.
    The brackets are used to show that the number of cents is given by the whole expression not just the last part.

2. g tiles weigh m kilograms. What would be the weight of:

    (a) 1 tile? $\frac{m}{g}$ **kg** .... ☞ Divide the weight by the number of tiles.

    (b) k tiles? $\frac{km}{g}$ .... ☞ Multiply the weight of 1 tile by the number of tiles.

3. If a carton holds e eggs:

    (a) how many eggs will fit in c cartons? .... ☞ Multiply the number of eggs in 1 carton by the number of cartons.
    ce eggs

    (b) how many cartons will be needed
    for j eggs? $\frac{j}{e}$ **cartons** .... ☞ Use numbers instead if you can't see the answer.

4. If a car travels at k kilometres per hour:

    (a) how far will it travel in 6 hours? **6k km** .... ☞ Multiply the speed by the number of hours.

    (b) how far will it travel in w hours? **kw km** .... ☞ Multiply the speed by the number of hours.

    (c) how long will it take to travel n kilometres?
    $\frac{n}{k}$ **hours**

    (d) If it still has p kilometres to travel after
    travelling for h hours, how long is the trip?
    (hk + p) km

5. A television program begins at b am and finishes at
    c pm the same day. How long does the program run?
    (12 − b + c) hours

6. If m and n are two different positive numbers, determine, if possible, whether the following are positive or negative:

   (a) $m + n$ **positive** .... ☞ Adding any two positive numbers will give a larger number.

   (b) $m - n$ If $m > n$, $m - n$ will be **positive**.
            If $m < n$, $m - n$ will be **negative**.

   (c) mn **positive** .... ☞ Two positives always multiply to a positive number.

   (d) $\frac{n}{m}$ **positive**

   (e) m^2 **positive** .... ☞ The square of any number, except zero, is positive.

   (f) $\frac{n^2}{m}$ **positive**

7. If p, q and r are consecutive numbers, with $p > q > r$, write an expression for:

   (a) q in terms of p. $q = p - 1$ .... ☞ The numbers are consecutive, so q is one less than p.

   (b) r in terms of p. $r = p - 2$ .... ☞ r is one less than q, two less than p.

   (c) $q^2 - pr$ $= (p - 1)^2 - p(p - 2)$ .... ☞ Replacing q and r with the above expressions.
               $= p^2 - 2 \times p \times 1 + 1^2 - p^2 + 2p$ .... ☞ Being careful with the signs.
               $= p^2 - 2p + 1 - p^2 + 2p$
               $= 1$ .... ☞ Collecting like terms.

8. Find a simple expression for (a) the perimeter, and (b) the area of this rectangle. (Measurements are in metres.)

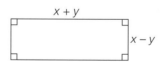

$x + y$

$x - y$

   (a) Perimeter $= \mathbf{2 \times length + 2 \times breadth}$ .... ☞ The perimeter is the sum of all the sides.
                   $= \mathbf{2(x + y) + 2(x - y)}$ Substituting the expressions for length and breadth.
                   $= \mathbf{2x + 2y + 2x - 2y}$ Removing brackets.
                   $= \mathbf{4x}$ Collecting like terms.
   The perimeter will be $\mathbf{4x}$ metres.

   (b) Area $= \mathbf{length \times breadth}$
           $= \mathbf{(x + y)(x - y)}$ .... ☞ Substituting.
           $= \mathbf{x^2 - y^2}$ Sum by difference.
   The area will be $\mathbf{(x^2 - y^2)}$ metres^2.

Simultaneous means 'occurring at the same time'.
When solving a pair of simultaneous equations, we find a solution that satisfies both equations at the same time.
If we have two equations (with two different pronumerals), there is only one solution that satisfies both equations simultaneously.

One method of solving this type of equation is by substitution.

Example:
Solve simultaneously $3x + 2y = 10$ and $y = x - 5$.

Solution:

$$3x + 2y = 10 \quad \text{(i)}$$
$$y = x - 5 \quad \text{(ii)}$$

We number the equations to help explain what we are doing.

Substitute (ii) into (i): $3x + 2(x - 5) = 10$
$$3x + 2x - 10 = 10$$
$$5x - 10 = 10$$
$$5x = 20$$
$$x = 4$$

We replace y in our first equation with the expression for y, which is our second equation.

Substitute into (ii): $y = 4 - 5$
$$y = -1$$
$$\therefore \ x = 4 \text{ and } y = -1.$$

We can substitute into either of the equations to find the value of the other pronumeral.

Remember: The subject of a formula or equation is the pronumeral found before the '=' sign. The subject of the equation $y = 7x - 8$ is y.

When both of a pair of simultaneous equations have the same subject, we solve the simultaneous equations by placing them equal to each other.

Example:
Solve simultaneously:
$y = 7x - 8$ and $y = -3x + 2$.

Solution:
$$7x - 8 = -3x + 2$$
$$7x = -3x + 10$$
$$10x = 10$$
$$x = 1$$
Substitute in $y = 7x - 8$
$$y = 7 \times 1 - 8$$
$$y = -1$$
$$\therefore \ x = 1 \text{ and } y = -1$$

It might be necessary to rearrange the equations before we can substitute.

Example:
Solve simultaneously:
$9x - 5y + 2 = 0$ and $x + 3y - 14 = 0$.

Solution:
$$9x - 5y + 2 = 0 \quad \text{(i)}$$
$$x + 3y - 14 = 0 \quad \text{(ii)}$$
Rearranging (ii): $x = -3y + 14$ (iii)
Substitute (iii) into (i): $9(-3y + 14) - 5y + 2 = 0$
$$-27y + 126 - 5y + 2 = 0$$
$$-32y + 128 = 0$$
$$-32y = -128$$
$$y = 4$$
Substitute into (iii): $x = -3 \times 4 + 14$
$$x = 2$$
$$\therefore \ x = 2 \text{ and } y = 4$$

1. **Solve simultaneously, by substitution:**

(a) $7x + 2y = 38$ and $y = 2x - 3$

_____

_____

_____

_____

_____

(b) $4a - 3b = 10$ and $a = 3b - 2$

_____

_____

_____

_____

_____

(c) $y = 8x - 3$ and $y = -2x + 7$

_____

_____

_____

_____

_____

(d) $y = 6x + 5$ and $y = 5x - 4$

_____

_____

_____

_____

_____

(e) $2p + 5q - 7 = 0$ and $p = q$

_____

_____

_____

_____

_____

_____

(f) $3x - 2y + 4 = 0$ and $y = x + 1$

_____

_____

_____

_____

_____

_____

(g) $7a + 3b - 2 = 0$ and $a - b = 6$

_____

_____

_____

_____

_____

_____

(h) $4p + q + 1 = 0$ and $3p - 2q + 20 = 0$

_____

_____

_____

_____

_____

_____

1. Solve simultaneously, by substitution:

(a) $7x + 2y = 38$ and $y = 2x - 3$

$\qquad\qquad 7x + 2y = 38$ $\qquad$ (i) ......☞ Write down both equations and number them.

$\qquad\qquad\quad y = 2x - 3$ $\qquad$ (ii)

Substitute (ii) into (i): $\mathbf{7x + 2(2x - 3) = 38}$ ......☞ We replace y in the first equation with the

$\qquad\qquad\qquad \mathbf{7x + 4x - 6 = 38}$ $\qquad\qquad\qquad$ expression for y that is the second equation.

$\qquad\qquad\qquad\qquad \mathbf{11x - 6 = 38}$ $\qquad\qquad\qquad$ We then solve this new equation.

$\qquad\qquad\qquad\qquad\quad \mathbf{11x = 44}$

$\qquad\qquad\qquad\qquad\qquad \mathbf{x = 4}$

Substitute into (ii): $\qquad\qquad \mathbf{y = 2 \times 4 - 3}$ ☞ Substitute the value of x into either of the original

$\qquad\qquad\qquad\qquad\qquad\quad \mathbf{y = 5}$ $\qquad\qquad\qquad$ equations and solve to find the value of y.

$\qquad\quad \therefore\ \mathbf{x = 4\ \ and\ \ y = 5}$ $\qquad\qquad\qquad$ Write down the solution.

(b) $4a - 3b = 10$ and $a = 3b - 2$

$\qquad\qquad\quad 4a - 3b = 10$ $\qquad$ (i) ......☞ Write down the two equations and number them.

$\qquad\qquad\qquad\quad a = 3b - 2$ $\qquad$ (ii)

Substitute (ii) into (i): $\mathbf{4(3b - 2) - 3b = 10}$

$\qquad\qquad\qquad \mathbf{12b - 8 - 3b = 10}$

$\qquad\qquad\qquad\qquad \mathbf{9b - 8 = 10}$ ......☞ Collecting like terms.

$\qquad\qquad\qquad\qquad\qquad \mathbf{9b = 18}$

$\qquad\qquad\qquad\qquad\qquad\quad \mathbf{b = 2}$

Substitute into (ii): $\qquad \mathbf{a = 3 \times 2 - 2}$ ......☞ We could substitute into either equation.

$\qquad\qquad\qquad\qquad\qquad \mathbf{a = 4}$

$\qquad\quad \therefore\ \mathbf{a = 4\ \ and\ \ b = 2}$ ......☞ Write down the solution.

(c) $y = 8x - 3$ and $y = -2x + 7$

$\qquad\qquad\quad \mathbf{8x - 3 = -2x + 7}$ ......☞ In this case place the equations equal to each other.

$\qquad\qquad\qquad \mathbf{8x = -2x + 10}$ $\qquad\qquad\qquad$ Adding 3 to both sides;

$\qquad\qquad\qquad \mathbf{10x = 10}$ $\qquad\qquad\qquad\qquad$ adding 2x to both sides.

$\qquad\qquad\qquad\quad \mathbf{x = 1}$

Substitute into $\qquad \mathbf{y = 8x - 3}$ ......☞ We could substitute into either of the equations.

$\qquad\qquad\qquad \mathbf{y = 8 \times 1 - 3}$

$\qquad\qquad\qquad\quad \mathbf{y = 5}$ ......☞ Check the answer by substituting into the other

$\qquad\quad \therefore\ \mathbf{x = 1\ \ and\ \ y = 5}$ $\qquad\qquad\qquad$ equation ($y = -2x + 7$).

(d) $y = 6x + 5$ and $y = 5x - 4$

$\qquad\qquad\quad \mathbf{6x + 5 = 5x - 4}$ ......☞ Place the equations equal to each other.

$\qquad\qquad\qquad \mathbf{6x = 5x - 9}$ $\qquad\qquad\qquad$ Subtracting 5 from both sides,

$\qquad\qquad\qquad\quad \mathbf{x = -9}$ $\qquad\qquad\qquad$ Subtracting 5x from both sides.

Substitute into $\qquad \mathbf{y = 6x + 5}$ $\qquad\qquad\qquad$ Substitute into either equation

$\qquad\qquad\qquad \mathbf{y = 6 \times -9 + 5}$ $\qquad\qquad\qquad$ and solve.

$\qquad\qquad\qquad\quad \mathbf{y = -49}$

$\qquad\quad \therefore\ \mathbf{x = -9\ \ and\ \ y = -49}$ ......☞ Write down the solution.

(e) $2p + 5q - 7 = 0$ and $p = q$

$$2p + 5q - 7 = 0 \qquad \text{(i)}$$
$$p = q \qquad \text{(ii)}$$

Substitute (ii) into (i): $2q + 5q - 7 = 0$ ☞ We could substitute for either p or q.
$$7q = 7$$
$$q = 1$$
Substitute into (ii): $p = 1$
$$\therefore \ p = 1 \text{ and } q = 1$$ ☞ Write down the solution.

(f) $3x - 2y + 4 = 0$ and $y = x + 1$

$$3x - 2y + 4 = 0 \qquad \text{(i)}$$
$$y = x + 1 \qquad \text{(ii)}$$

Substitute (ii) into (i): $3x - 2(x + 1) + 4 = 0$
$$3x - 2x - 2 + 4 = 0$$
$$x + 2 = 0$$ ☞ Collecting like terms.
$$x = -2$$
Substitute into (ii): $y = -2 + 1$
$$y = -1$$
$$\therefore \ x = -2 \text{ and } y = -1$$ ☞ Write down the solution.

(g) $7a + 3b - 2 = 0$ and $a - b = 6$

$$7a + 3b - 2 = 0 \qquad \text{(i)}$$ ☞ We need to rearrange equation (ii)
$$a - b = 6 \qquad \text{(ii)}$$ before we can substitute.
Rearranging (ii): $a = b + 6$ (iii) (Add b to both sides of the equation.)
Substitute (iii) into (i): $7(b + 6) + 3b - 2 = 0$
$$7b + 42 + 3b - 2 = 0$$
$$10b + 40 = 0$$ ☞ Collecting like terms.
$$10b = -40$$
$$b = -4$$
Substitute into (iii): $a = -4 + 6$ ☞ It is easier to substitute into (iii).
$$a = 2$$
$$\therefore \ a = 2 \text{ and } b = -4$$

(h) $4p + q + 1 = 0$ and $3p - 2q + 20 = 0$

$$4p + q + 1 = 0 \qquad \text{(i)}$$
$$3p - 2q + 20 = 0 \qquad \text{(ii)}$$
Rearranging (i): $q = -4p - 1$ (iii) ☞ It is easier to rearrange (i) to make q the subject.
Substitute (iii) into (ii): $3p - 2(-4p - 1) + 20 = 0$
$$3p + 8p + 2 + 20 = 0$$ ☞ Removing grouping symbols and watching the signs.
$$11p + 22 = 0$$
$$11p = -22$$
$$p = -2$$
Substitute into (iii): $q = -4 \times -2 - 1$
$$q = 7$$
$$\therefore \ p = -2 \text{ and } q = 7$$

> Eliminate means 'to get rid of'.
> In some pairs of simultaneous equations, adding the two equations together will eliminate one of the pronumerals.
> We can then solve a simple equation to find the value of the remaining pronumeral.
> We must be careful to add every part of the equations.

Example:
Solve the pair of simultaneous equations: $x + y = 9$
$x - y = 3$

Solution:

$x + y = 9$ (i)	Write down the equations, under one another,
$x - y = 3$ (ii)	and number them.
(i) + (ii): $2x = 12$	Add each part: $x + x = 2x$, $y + (-y) = 0$, $9 + 3 = 12$.
$x = 6$	Solve the resulting equation.
Substitute into (i): $6 + y = 9$	We could substitute into either equation.
$y = 3$	
$\therefore \ x = 6$ and $y = 3$	Write down the solution.

> It's a good idea to check the solution in the second equation (the one that wasn't used in the substitution step).
> There's no need to write anything down, just do a mental check.
> If the solution satisfies the second equation, you know you have the right answer.
> If it doesn't work, you've done something wrong!

Example:
Solve the simultaneous equations: (a) $3a - b = 13$ (b) $7x + 2y + 1 = 0$
$5a + b = 19$ $3x - 2y - 11 = 0$

Solution:

(a)

$$3a - b = 13 \quad \text{(i)}$$
$$5a + b = 19 \quad \text{(ii)}$$

(i) + (ii): $8a = 32$
$a = 4$

Substitute in (i): $3 \times 4 - b = 13$
$12 - b = 13$
$-b = 1$
$b = -1$
$\therefore \ a = 4$ and $b = -1$

(b)

$$7x + 2y + 1 = 0 \quad \text{(i)}$$
$$3x - 2y - 11 = 0 \quad \text{(ii)}$$

(i) + (ii): $10x - 10 = 0$
$10x = 10$
$x = 1$

Substitute in (i): $7 \times 1 + 2y + 1 = 0$
$2y + 8 = 0$
$2y = -8$
$y = -4$
$\therefore \ x = 1$ and $y = -4$

1. Solve the simultaneous equations (by adding to eliminate one of the pronumerals):

(a) $x + y = 11$ and $x - y = 7$

(b) $7a + b = 13$ and $3a - b = 7$

(c) $5p + 2q = 11$ and $3p - 2q = -3$

(d) $9y - 5z = 3$ and $4y + 5z = 88$

(e) $-g + 5h = 26$ and $g - 3h = -14$

(f) $7m - t - 12 = 0$ and $5m + t = 0$

(g) $4c - 3d + 20 = 0$ and $c + 3d - 10 = 0$

(h) $8x + 9y + 17 = 0$ and $2x - 9y - 7 = 0$

1. Solve the simultaneous equations (by adding to eliminate one of the pronumerals):

(a) $x + y = 11$ and $x - y = 7$

$$x + y = 11 \quad \text{(i)}$$
$$x - y = 7 \quad \text{(ii)}$$

(i) + (ii): $\quad 2x = 18$ .... ☞ Add the equations together, term by term.

☞ Write down the equations and number them.

$$x = 9$$ Solving this new equation.

Substitute into (i): $9 + y = 11$ We could substitute into either of the equations.

$$y = 2$$

$\therefore x = 9$ and $y = 2$ .... ☞ Write down the solution.

Check by substituting into (ii), $9 - 2 = 7$ ✓

(b) $7a + b = 13$ and $3a - b = 7$

$$7a + b = 13 \quad \text{(i)}$$ ☞ Write down both equations and number them.
$$3a - b = 7 \quad \text{(ii)}$$

(i) + (ii): $\quad 10a = 20$

Add the equations together, term by term.

$$a = 2$$

Substitute into (i): $7 \times 2 + b = 13$

$$14 + b = 13$$ .... ☞ Solving this new equation.

$$b = -1$$

$\therefore a = 2$ and $b = -1$ .... ☞ Write down the solution.

Check by substituting into (ii), $3 \times 2 - (-1) = 7$ ✓

(c) $5p + 2q = 11$ and $3p - 2q = -3$

$$5p + 2q = 11 \quad \text{(i)}$$
$$3p - 2q = -3 \quad \text{(ii)}$$

(i) + (ii): $\quad 8p = 8$ .... ☞ $5p + 3p = 8p$, $2q + (-2q) = 0$, $11 + (-3) = 8$

$$p = 1$$

Substitute into (i): $5 \times 1 + 2q = 11$

$$5 + 2q = 11$$
$$2q = 6$$
$$q = 3$$

$\therefore p = 1$ and $q = 3$ .... ☞ Check: $3 \times 1 - 2 \times 3 = -3$ ✓

(d) $9y - 5z = 3$ and $4y + 5z = 88$

$$9y - 5z = 3 \quad \text{(i)}$$
$$4y + 5z = 88 \quad \text{(ii)}$$

(i) + (ii): $\quad 13y = 91$

$$y = 7$$

Substitute into (ii): $4 \times 7 + 5z = 88$

$$28 + 5z = 88$$
$$5z = 60$$
$$z = 12$$

$\therefore y = 7$ and $z = 12$

(e) $-g + 5h = 26$ and $g - 3h = -14$

$$-g + 5h = 26 \quad \text{(i)} \quad \text{☞ Write down the equations and number them.}$$
$$g - 3h = -14 \quad \text{(ii)}$$

(i) + (ii): $\quad 2h = 12$ ☞ In this case the first pronumeral is eliminated.
$$h = 6$$

Substitute into (ii): $g - 3 \times 6 = -14$ ☞ We could substitute into either equation.
$$g - 18 = -14$$
$$g = 4$$

$\therefore\ g = 4$ and $h = 6$ ☞ Write down the solution.

Check in (i): $-4 + 5 \times 6 = 26$ ✓

(f) $7m - t - 12 = 0$ and $5m + t = 0$

$$7m - t - 12 = 0 \quad \text{(i)} \quad \text{☞ You may like to write the like terms}$$
$$5m + t = 0 \quad \text{(ii)} \quad \text{under one another to make it clear.}$$

(i) + (ii): $\quad 12m - 12 = 0$ ☞ Add each term.
$$12m = 12$$
$$m = 1$$

Substitute into (ii): $5 \times 1 + t = 0$
$$5 + t = 0$$
$$t = -5$$

$\therefore\ m = 1$ and $t = -5$

(g) $4c - 3d + 20 = 0$ and $c + 3d - 10 = 0$

$$4c - 3d + 20 = 0 \quad \text{(i)}$$
$$c + 3d - 10 = 0 \quad \text{(ii)}$$

(i) + (ii): $\quad 5c + 10 = 0$
$$5c = -10$$
$$c = -2$$

Substitute into (ii): $-2 + 3d - 10 = 0$
$$3d = 12$$
$$d = 4$$

$\therefore\ c = -2$ and $d = 4$ ☞ Write down the solution. (Don't forget to check.)

(h) $8x + 9y + 17 = 0$ and $2x - 9y - 7 = 0$

$$8x + 9y + 17 = 0 \quad \text{(i)}$$
$$2x - 9y - 7 = 0 \quad \text{(ii)}$$

(i) + (ii): $\quad 10x + 10 = 0$
$$10x = -10$$
$$x = -1$$

Substitute into (i): $8 \times -1 + 9y + 17 = 0$ ☞ We can substitute into either equation.
$$9y + 9 = 0$$
$$9y = -9$$
$$y = -1$$

$\therefore\ x = -1$ and $y = -1$

In an algebraic expression, the number in front of a pronumeral is called its coefficient. The coefficient of $2x$ is 2. The coefficient of $9a^5$ is 9, the coefficient of $-7k^3$ is -7.

In the expression $4x^2 - 5x + 7$, the coefficient of x^2 is 4, but the coefficient of x is -5, because we could rewrite this expression as $4x^2 + (-5x) + 7$.

If the coefficients of one of the pairs of pronumerals in a pair of simultaneous equations are exactly the same, we can eliminate that pronumeral by subtracting the equations.

Example:
Solve simultaneously $6p + q = 17$ and $4p + q = 13$.

Solution:

$6p + q = 17$ (i)	Write down the two equations and number them.
$4p + q = 13$ (ii)	
(i) – (ii): $2p = 4$	Subtract. $(6p - 4p = 2p, \quad q - q = 0, \quad 17 - 13 = 4)$
$p = 2$	Solve the resulting equation.
Substitute into (i): $6 \times 2 + q = 17$	Substitute into either equation.
$12 + q = 17$	Solve this new equation.
$q = 5$	
$\therefore \; p = 2$ and $q = 5$	Write the solution. (Don't forget to check mentally.)

It doesn't matter which pronumeral we eliminate, or which equation we subtract from the other.
Be very careful when subtracting, particularly where negatives are involved.

Example:
Solve simultaneously: (a) $5a - 9b = -3$ (b) $3y - 8z = 0$
                             $5a + 4b = 23$ $y - 8z + 16 = 0$

Solution:

(a)
$$5a - 9b = -3 \qquad \text{(i)}$$
$$5a + 4b = 23 \qquad \text{(ii)}$$
(ii) – (i): $\qquad 13b = 26 \quad [4b - (-9b) = 13b]$
$$b = 2$$
Substitute in (i): $5a - 9 \times 2 = -3$
$$5a - 18 = -3$$
$$5a = 15$$
$$a = 3$$
$$\therefore \; a = 3 \text{ and } b = 2$$

(b)
$$3y - 8z = 0 \qquad \text{(i)}$$
$$y - 8z + 16 = 0 \qquad \text{(ii)}$$
(i) – (ii): $\qquad 2y - 16 = 0$
$$2y = 16$$
$$y = 8$$
Substitute in (i): $3 \times 8 - 8z = 0$
$$24 - 8z = 0$$
$$-8z = -24$$
$$z = 3$$
$$\therefore \; y = 8 \text{ and } z = 3$$

1. Solve the simultaneous equations (by subtracting to eliminate one of the pronumerals):

(a) $5a + b = 17$ and $3a + b = 11$

(b) $6g - h = 33$ and $5g - h = 28$

(c) $5p + 3q = 11$ and $8p + 3q = 5$

(d) $7x + 4y - 27 = 0$ and $2x + 4y - 22 = 0$

(e) $5y - 7z = -18$ and $5y + 3z = 22$

(f) $9m - 2n - 42 = 0$ and $5m - 2n - 26 = 0$

(g) $7a + 2x + 11 = 0$ and $7a - 3x + 1 = 0$

(h) $8e - k - 42 = 0$ and $e - k = 0$

1. Solve the simultaneous equations (by subtracting to eliminate one of the pronumerals):

(a) $5a + b = 17$ and $3a + b = 11$

$$5a + b = 17 \qquad \text{(i)} \qquad \text{☞ Write down the equations and number them.}$$
$$3a + b = 11 \qquad \text{(ii)}$$

(i) – (ii): $2a = 6$ ☞ Subtract either equation from the other.

$$a = 3$$

Substitute into (ii): $3 \times 3 + b = 11$ ☞ We can substitute into either equation.

$$9 + b = 11$$
$$b = 2$$

$\therefore\ a = 3\ \text{ and }\ b = 2$ ☞ Write down the solution.

Check the solution in (i): $5 \times 3 + 2 = 17$ ✓

(b) $6g - h = 33$ and $5g - h = 28$

$$6g - h = 33 \qquad \text{(i)} \qquad \text{☞ Write down the equations and number them.}$$
$$5g - h = 28 \qquad \text{(ii)}$$

(i) – (ii): $g = 5$ ☞ $6g - 5g = g;\ -h - (-h) = 0$

Substitute into (i): $6 \times 5 - h = 33$ ☞ We could substitute into either equation.

$$30 - h = 33$$
$$-h = 3$$
$$h = -3$$

$\therefore\ g = 5\ \text{ and }\ h = -3$ ☞ Check in (ii): $5 \times 5 - (-3) = 28$ ✓

(c) $5p + 3q = 11$ and $8p + 3q = 5$

$$5p + 3q = 11 \qquad \text{(i)} \qquad \text{☞ The coefficients of } q \text{ are the same.}$$
$$8p + 3q = 5 \qquad \text{(ii)} \qquad \text{☞ Subtract either equation from the other.}$$

(ii) – (i): $3p = -6$

$$p = -2$$

Substitute into (i): $5 \times -2 + 3q = 11$

$$-10 + 3q = 11$$
$$3q = 21$$
$$q = 7$$

$\therefore\ p = -2\ \text{ and }\ q = 7$ ☞ Write down the solution. (Don't forget to check.)

(d) $7x + 4y - 27 = 0$ and $2x + 4y - 22 = 0$

$$7x + 4y - 27 = 0 \qquad \text{(i)}$$
$$2x + 4y - 22 = 0 \qquad \text{(ii)}$$

(i) – (ii): $5x - 5 = 0$ ☞ Be careful subtracting negative numbers.

$$5x = 5$$
$$x = 1$$

Substitute into (ii): $2 \times 1 + 4y - 22 = 0$

$$4y - 20 = 0$$
$$4y = 20$$
$$y = 5$$

$\therefore\ x = 1\ \text{ and }\ y = 5$ ☞ Write down the solution.

(e) $5y - 7z = -18$ and $5y + 3z = 22$

$$5y - 7z = -18 \quad \text{(i)}$$ ☞ Write down the equations and number them.
$$5y + 3z = 22 \quad \text{(ii)}$$

(ii) − (i): $\mathbf{10z = 40}$ ☞ In this case the first pronumeral is eliminated. We get the same result no matter which equation is subtracted from the other.

$$\mathbf{z = 4}$$

Substitute into (ii): $\mathbf{5y + 3 \times 4 = 22}$

$$\mathbf{5y + 12 = 22}$$
$$\mathbf{5y = 10}$$
$$\mathbf{y = 2}$$

$$\therefore \ \mathbf{y = 2 \ and \ z = 4}$$ ☞ Check in (i): $5 \times 2 - 7 \times 4 = -18$ ✓

(f) $9m - 2n - 42 = 0$ and $5m - 2n - 26 = 0$

$$9m - 2n - 42 = 0 \quad \text{(i)}$$
$$5m - 2n - 26 = 0 \quad \text{(ii)}$$

(i) − (ii): $\mathbf{4m - 16 = 0}$

$$\mathbf{4m = 16}$$
$$\mathbf{m = 4}$$

Substitute into (ii): $\mathbf{5 \times 4 - 2n - 26 = 0}$ ☞ We can substitute into either equation.

$$\mathbf{-2n - 6 = 0}$$
$$\mathbf{-2n = 6}$$
$$\mathbf{n = -3}$$

$$\therefore \ \mathbf{m = 4 \ and \ n = -3}$$

(g) $7a + 2x + 11 = 0$ and $7a - 3x + 1 = 0$ ☞ The coefficients of a are the same, so a will be eliminated.

$$7a + 2x + 11 = 0 \quad \text{(i)}$$
$$7a - 3x + 1 = 0 \quad \text{(ii)}$$

(i) − (ii): $\mathbf{5x + 10 = 0}$

$$\mathbf{5x = -10}$$
$$\mathbf{x = -2}$$

Substitute into (ii): $\mathbf{7a - 3 \times -2 + 1 = 0}$

$$\mathbf{7a + 7 = 0}$$
$$\mathbf{7a = -7}$$
$$\mathbf{a = -1}$$

$$\therefore \ \mathbf{a = -1 \ and \ x = -2}$$

(h) $8e - k - 42 = 0$ and $e - k = 0$

$$8e - k - 42 = 0 \quad \text{(i)}$$
$$e - k = 0 \quad \text{(ii)}$$

(i) − (ii): $\mathbf{7e - 42 = 0}$

$$\mathbf{7e = 42}$$
$$\mathbf{e = 6}$$

Substitute into (ii): $\mathbf{6 - k = 0}$

$$\mathbf{k = 6}$$

$$\therefore \ \mathbf{e = 6 \ and \ k = 6}$$ ☞ Don't forget to check the solution.

We have solved simultaneous equations using the elimination method by both adding and subtracting.
We saw that if two terms had the same coefficient, they could be eliminated by subtracting.
You may have noticed that we added the two equations to eliminate a pronumeral when the coefficients of that pronumeral were opposites (the 'same' number but with a different sign).
We use this knowledge to decide whether we add or subtract to solve a pair of simultaneous equations.

If the coefficients are exactly the same, subtract. If the coefficients are opposites, add.

Ask yourself:
- Which terms can I eliminate?
- Are the coefficients the same or are they opposites?
- Do I add or subtract?

Example:
Solve simultaneously:

(a) $9x - 5y = 64$
$7x - 5y = 52$

(b) $5a - 3b - 25 = 0$
$2a + 3b - 10 = 0$

Solution:

(a)

$$9x - 5y = 64 \quad \text{(i)}$$
$$7x - 5y = 52 \quad \text{(ii)}$$

(i) − (ii): $\quad 2x = 12$
$\qquad\qquad x = 6$

Substitute in (i): $\quad 9 \times 6 - 5y = 64$
$$54 - 5y = 64$$
$$-5y = 10$$
$$y = -2$$
$$\therefore \ x = 6 \ \text{ and } \ y = -2$$

(b)

$$5a - 3b - 25 = 0 \quad \text{(i)}$$
$$2a + 3b - 10 = 0 \quad \text{(ii)}$$

(i) + (ii): $\quad 7a - 35 = 0$
$$7a = 35$$
$$a = 5$$

Substitute in (i): $\quad 5 \times 5 - 3b - 25 = 0$
$$25 - 3b - 25 = 0$$
$$-3b = 0$$
$$b = 0$$
$$\therefore \ a = 5 \ \text{ and } \ b = 0$$

Always add, or subtract, **every** term to make sure that one pronumeral does, in fact, disappear!

Example:
Solve simultaneously:

(a) $6k + 7m = 10$
$11k + 7m = -5$

(b) $3c + 4d = -10$
$c - 4d = 2$

Solution:

(a)

$$6k + 7m = 10 \quad \text{(i)}$$
$$11k + 7m = -5 \quad \text{(ii)}$$

(ii) − (i): $\quad 5k = -15$
$$k = -3$$

Substitute in (i): $\quad 6 \times -3 + 7m = 10$
$$-18 + 7m = 10$$
$$7m = 28$$
$$m = 4$$
$$\therefore \ k = -3 \ \text{ and } \ m = 4$$

(b)

$$3c + 4d = -10 \quad \text{(i)}$$
$$c - 4d = 2 \quad \text{(ii)}$$

(i) + (ii): $\quad 4c = -8$
$$c = -2$$

Substitute in (ii): $\quad -2 - 4d = 2$
$$-4d = 4$$
$$d = -1$$
$$\therefore \ c = -2 \ \text{ and } \ d = -1$$

1. Use the elimination method to solve these simultaneous equations:

   (a) $7x + y = 41$ and $x + y = 5$

   (b) $8a + b = 59$ and $5a - b = 32$

   (c) $6m - 5n = -37$ and $2m - 5n = -29$

   (d) $9e - 6f = -51$ and $4e + 6f = 12$

   (e) $11p + 3q - 65 = 0$ and $8p - 3q - 11 = 0$

   (f) $12x - 7y + 57 = 0$ and $5x - 7y + 36 = 0$

   (g) $x + 2y + 5 = 0$ and $x - 3y - 5 = 0$

   (h) $6q + 5w = 28$ and $6q - 5w = 8$

ELIMINATION METHOD Worked Solutions

1. Use the elimination method to solve these simultaneous equations:

(a) $7x + y = 41$ and $x + y = 5$

$$7x + y = 41 \quad \text{(i)}$$ ☞ Write down the equations and number them.
$$x + y = 5 \quad \text{(ii)}$$

(i) − (ii): $\quad 6x = 36$ ☞ The coefficients of y are the same, so we subtract.
$$x = 6$$

Substitute into (ii): $6 + y = 5$ ☞ We can substitute into either equation.
$$y = -1$$
$$\therefore x = 6 \text{ and } y = -1$$ ☞ Write down the answer. (Check the solution.)

(b) $8a + b = 59$ and $5a - b = 32$

$$8a + b = 59 \quad \text{(i)}$$ ☞ Write down the equations and number them.
$$5a - b = 32 \quad \text{(ii)}$$

(i) + (ii): $\quad 13a = 91$ ☞ The coefficients of b are opposites, so we add.
$$a = 7$$

Substitute into (i): $8 \times 7 + b = 59$ ☞ We can substitute into either equation.
$$56 + b = 59$$
$$b = 3$$
$$\therefore a = 7 \text{ and } b = 3$$ ☞ Check in (ii), $5 \times 7 - 3 = 32$ ✓

(c) $6m - 5n = -37$ and $2m - 5n = -29$

$$6m - 5n = -37 \quad \text{(i)}$$ ☞ Write down the equations and number them.
$$2m - 5n = -29 \quad \text{(ii)}$$

(i) − (ii): $\quad 4m = -8$ ☞ The coefficients of n are the same so we subtract.
$$m = -2$$

Substitute into (ii): $2 \times -2 - 5n = -29$
$$-4 - 5n = -29$$
$$-5n = -25$$
$$n = 5$$
$$\therefore m = -2 \text{ and } n = 5$$ ☞ Write down the solution.

(d) $9e - 6f = -51$ and $4e + 6f = 12$

$$9e - 6f = -51 \quad \text{(i)}$$
$$4e + 6f = 12 \quad \text{(ii)}$$

(i) + (ii): $\quad 13e = -39$ ☞ The coefficients of f are opposites, so we add.
$$e = -3$$

Substitute into (ii): $4 \times -3 + 6f = 12$
$$-12 + 6f = 12$$
$$6f = 24$$
$$f = 4$$
$$\therefore e = -3 \text{ and } f = 4$$ ☞ Don't forget to check the solution.

(e) $11p + 3q - 65 = 0$ and $8p - 3q - 11 = 0$

$$11p + 3q - 65 = 0 \quad \text{(i)}$$
$$8p - 3q - 11 = 0 \quad \text{(ii)}$$

☞ Write down the equations and number them.

(i) + (ii): $\quad 19p - 76 = 0$

☞ The coefficients of q are opposites, so we add.

$$19p = 76$$
$$p = 4$$

Substitute into (i): $\quad 11 \times 4 + 3q - 65 = 0$

☞ We can substitute into either equation.

$$3q - 21 = 0$$
$$3q = 21$$
$$q = 7$$
$$\therefore \ p = 4 \ \text{and} \ q = 7$$

☞ Write down the solution.

(f) $12x - 7y + 57 = 0$ and $5x - 7y + 36 = 0$

$$12x - 7y + 57 = 0 \quad \text{(i)}$$
$$5x - 7y + 36 = 0 \quad \text{(ii)}$$

(i) − (ii): $\quad 7x + 21 = 0$

☞ The coefficients of y are the same, so we subtract.

$$7x = -21$$
$$x = -3$$

Substitute into (ii): $\quad 5 \times -3 - 7y + 36 = 0$
$$-7y + 21 = 0$$
$$-7y = -21$$
$$y = 3$$
$$\therefore \ x = -3 \ \text{and} \ y = 3$$

☞ Don't forget to check the solution.

(g) $x + 2y + 5 = 0$ and $x - 3y - 5 = 0$

$$x + 2y + 5 = 0 \quad \text{(i)}$$
$$x - 3y - 5 = 0 \quad \text{(ii)}$$

(i) − (ii): $\quad 5y + 10 = 0$

☞ The coefficients of x are the same, so we subtract.

$$5y = -10$$
$$y = -2$$

Substitute into (i): $x + 2 \times -2 + 5 = 0$
$$x + 1 = 0$$
$$x = -1$$
$$\therefore \ x = -1 \ \text{and} \ y = -2$$

☞ Write down the solution.

(h) $6q + 5w = 28$ and $6q - 5w = 8$

☞ (We can either add or subtract these equations.)

$$6q + 5w = 28 \quad \text{(i)}$$
$$6q - 5w = 8 \quad \text{(ii)}$$

(i) + (ii): $\quad 12q = 36$
$$q = 3$$

Substitute into (i): $6 \times 3 + 5w = 28$
$$5w = 10$$
$$w = 2$$
$$\therefore \ q = 3 \ \text{and} \ w = 2$$

OR

$$6q + 5w = 28 \quad \text{(i)}$$
$$6q - 5w = 8 \quad \text{(ii)}$$

(i) − (ii): $\quad 10w = 20$
$$w = 2$$

Substitute into (i): $6q + 5 \times 2 = 28$
$$6q = 18$$
$$q = 3$$
$$\therefore \ q = 3 \ \text{and} \ w = 2$$

HARDER ELIMINATION METHOD Summary

In all the simultaneous equations we have so far solved by the elimination method,
a pair of pronumerals have had equal or opposite coefficients.
If, in a pair of simultaneous equations, no pronumerals have equal coefficients, we can multiply one or
both equations so that the coefficients become equal.

Consider the equations $3p - 5q + 7 = 0$ and $7p - 2q - 61 = 0$.
To eliminate q we need the coefficients to be the same.

Ask yourself:
- Into what number do both 5 and 2 divide? **10**
- What must we multiply 5 by to get 10? **2**
  So we multiply the first equation by 2.
- What must we multiply 2 by to get 10? **5**
  So we multiply the second equation by 5.

It's just like getting a common denominator!

Example:
Solve simultaneously the equations $3p - 5q + 7 = 0$ **and** $7p - 2q - 61 = 0$.

Solution:

$$3p - 5q + 7 = 0 \quad \text{(i)}$$
Write down the equations and number them.
$$7p - 2q - 61 = 0 \quad \text{(ii)}$$

(i) × 2: $\quad 6p - 10q + 14 = 0 \quad$ (iii)   Multiply the 1st equation by 2.

(ii) × 5: $\quad 35p - 10q - 305 = 0 \quad$ (iv)   Multiply the 2nd equation by 5.

(iv) − (iii): $\quad 29p - 319 = 0$ We now have 2 equations that can be solved by subtracting.

$$29p = 319$$
$$p = 11$$

Substitute in (i): $\;3 \times 11 - 5q + 7 = 0$ It is usually easier to substitute in one of the original equations.

$$33 - 5q + 7 = 0$$
$$-5q = -40$$
$$q = 8$$ Notice how the Roman numerals help to explain what

$$\therefore \; p = 11 \quad \text{and} \quad q = 8$$ we are doing.

We must take care when multiplying to multiply every part of the equation.

Example:
Solve simultaneously: **(a)** $\;7x + 3y = 23$ **(b)** $\;7x - 6y = 61$

$\qquad\qquad\qquad\qquad\qquad x + y = 5 \qquad\qquad\qquad\qquad\qquad 4x + 9y = 10$

Solution:

(a)
$$7x + 3y = 23 \quad \text{(i)}$$
$$x + y = 5 \quad \text{(ii)}$$

(ii) × 3: $\quad 3x + 3y = 15 \quad$ (iii)

(i) − (iii): $\quad 4x = 8$

$$x = 2$$

Substitute in (ii): $\;2 + y = 5$

$$y = 3$$

$$\therefore \; x = 2 \quad \text{and} \quad y = 3$$

(b)
$$7x - 6y = 61 \quad \text{(i)}$$
$$4x + 9y = 10 \quad \text{(ii)}$$

(i) × 3: $\quad 21x - 18y = 183 \quad$ (iii)

(ii) × 2: $\quad 8x + 18y = 20 \quad$ (iv)

(iii) + (iv): $\quad 29x = 203$

$$x = 7$$

Substitute in (i) $\;7 \times 7 - 6y = 61$

$$49 - 6y = 61$$
$$-6y = 12$$
$$y = -2$$

$$\therefore \; x = 7 \quad \text{and} \quad y = -2$$

34

1. Solve these simultaneous equations by elimination:

(a) $7x + 2y = 38$ and $3x + y = 17$

(b) $6a - 5b = 10$ and $2a + b = 14$

(c) $4y + 5z = -16$ and $y - 3z = 30$

(d) $11h - 2k = 95$ and $7h - 6k = 51$

(e) $8p - 3q = 40$ and $5p - 2q = 26$

(f) $4c + 7d = -3$ and $3c - 4d = 7$

(g) $10e + 3f + 2 = 0$ and $9e + 5f - 12 = 0$

(h) $5k - 2t - 1 = 0$ and $3k + 5t - 44 = 0$

1. Solve these simultaneous equations, by elimination:

(a) $7x + 2y = 38$ and $3x + y = 17$

$7x + 2y = 38$	(i)
$3x + y = 17$	(ii)
(ii) × 2: $\quad 6x + 2y = 34$	(iii)
(i) − (iii): $\quad\quad\quad x = 4$	

Substitute in (ii): $\quad 3 \times 4 + y = 17$
$$12 + y = 17$$
$$y = 5$$
$$\therefore \ x = 4 \ \text{ and } \ y = 5$$

☞ Write down the equations and number them.

☞ If we multiply equation (ii) by 2, the coefficients of y will be the same. We must multiply every term.

☞ Equation (ii) is the easiest to solve after we substitute.

☞ Write down the solution. (Don't forget to check!)

(b) $6a − 5b = 10$ and $2a + b = 14$

$6a − 5b = 10$	(i)
$2a + b = 14$	(ii)
(ii) × 5: $\quad 10a + 5b = 70$	(iii)
(i) + (iii): $\quad\quad 16a = 80$	

$$a = 5$$

Substitute into (ii): $\quad 2 \times 5 + b = 14$
$$10 + b = 14$$
$$b = 4$$
$$\therefore \ a = 5 \ \text{ and } \ b = 4$$

☞ Write down the equations and number them.

☞ Multiplying the second equation by 5 means that the coefficients of b in (i) and (iii) are now opposites.

(c) $4y + 5z = −16$ and $y − 3z = 30$

$4y + 5z = −16$	(i)
$y − 3z = 30$	(ii)
(ii) × 4: $\quad 4y − 12z = 120$	(iii)
(i) − (iii): $\quad\quad 17z = −136$	

$$z = −8$$

Substitute into (ii): $\quad y − 3 \times −8 = 30$
$$y + 24 = 30$$
$$y = 6$$
$$\therefore \ y = 6 \ \text{ and } \ z = −8$$

☞ It is easiest to make the coefficients of y equal. Don't forget to number this new equation.

☞ Check in (i): $\quad 4 \times 6 + 5 \times −8 = −16$ ✓

(d) $11h − 2k = 95$ and $7h − 6k = 51$

$11h − 2k = 95$	(i)
$7h − 6k = 51$	(ii)
(i) × 3: $\quad 33h − 6k = 285$	(iii)
(iii) − (ii): $\quad\quad 26h = 234$	

$$h = 9$$

Substitute into (i): $\quad 11 \times 9 − 2k = 95$
$$99 − 2k = 95$$
$$−2k = −4$$
$$k = 2$$
$$\therefore \ h = 9 \ \text{ and } \ k = 2$$

☞ It is easiest to multiply the first equation this time. We could have subtracted (iii) from (ii).

(e) $8p - 3q = 40$ and $5p - 2q = 26$

$8p - 3q = 40$ (i) ☞ Write down the equations and number them.

$5p - 2q = 26$ (ii)

(i) × 2: $16p - 6q = 80$ (iii) ☞ We must multiply both equations to get equal

(ii) × 3: $15p - 6q = 78$ (iv)   coefficients. We could make the coefficients of

(iii) − (iv): $p = 2$ either p or q equal.

Substitute into (ii): $5 \times 2 - 2q = 26$

$10 - 2q = 26$

$-2q = 16$

$q = -8$

$\therefore p = 2$ and $q = -8$ ☞ Don't forget to check the solution.

(f) $4c + 7d = -3$ and $3c - 4d = 7$

$4c + 7d = -3$ (i)

$3c - 4d = 7$ (ii)

(i) × 4: $16c + 28d = -12$ (iii) ☞ Be careful to multiply every term of each

(ii) × 7: $21c - 28d = 49$ (iv)   of the equations.

(iii) + (iv): $37c = 37$

$c = 1$

Substitute into (i): $4 \times 1 + 7d = -3$

$4 + 7d = -3$

$7d = -7$

$d = -1$

$\therefore c = 1$ and $d = -1$ ☞ Write down the solution.

(g) $10e + 3f + 2 = 0$ and $9e + 5f - 12 = 0$

$10e + 3f + 2 = 0$ (i)

$9e + 5f - 12 = 0$ (ii)

(i) × 5: $50e + 15f + 10 = 0$ (iii)

(ii) × 3: $27e + 15f - 36 = 0$ (iv)

(iii) − (iv): $23e + 46 = 0$

$23e = -46$

$e = -2$

Substitute into (i): $10 \times -2 + 3f + 2 = 0$

$3f - 18 = 0$

$3f = 18$

$f = 6$

$\therefore e = -2$ and $f = 6$

(h) $5k - 2t - 1 = 0$ and $3k + 5t - 44 = 0$

$5k - 2t - 1 = 0$ (i)

$3k + 5t - 44 = 0$ (ii)

(i) × 5: $25k - 10t - 5 = 0$ (iii)

(ii) × 2: $6k + 10t - 88 = 0$ (iv)

(iii) + (iv): $31k - 93 = 0$

$31k = 93$

$k = 3$

Substitute into (ii): $3 \times 3 + 5t - 44 = 0$

$5t - 35 = 0$

$5t = 35$

$t = 7$

$\therefore k = 3$ and $t = 7$

Another way to solve simultaneous equations is to draw the graph of each equation and find where they intersect. (Here, we are only dealing with the equations of straight lines.)

Example:

Complete each table of values and graph the line on a grid:

(a) $y = x + 4$

x	−1	0	1
y			

(b) $y = 3x − 4$

x	1	2	3
y			

(c) $x + y = 3$

x	0	1	2
y			

Solution:

(a) $y = x + 4$

x	−1	0	1
y	3	4	5

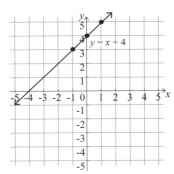

(b) $y = 3x − 4$

x	1	2	3
y	−1	2	5

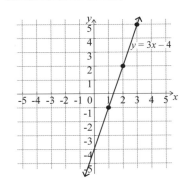

(c) $x + y = 3$

x	0	1	2
y	3	2	1

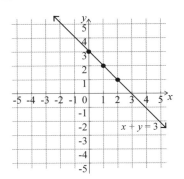

We can find the solution to a pair of simultaneous equations by graphing both equations on a grid and finding the point of intersection.

(We usually write the answer as a point. A solution of (2, 5) means that $x = 2$ and $y = 5$.)

Example:

Find graphically the solution of the simultaneous equations:

(a) $y = 3x − 1$ and $y = x + 3$ **(b)** $y = x − 4$ and $x + y = 4$ **(c)** $y = 2x + 2$ and $x − y = 1$

Solution:

(a) $y = 3x − 1$

x	0	1	2
y	−1	2	5

$y = x + 3$

x	0	1	2
y	3	4	5

(b) $y = x − 4$

x	0	1	2
y	−4	−3	−2

$x + y = 4$

x	0	1	2
y	4	3	2

(c) $y = 2x + 2$

x	0	1	2
y	2	4	6

$x − y = 1$

x	0	1	2
y	−1	0	1

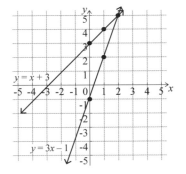

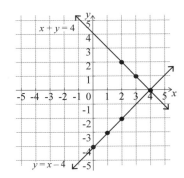

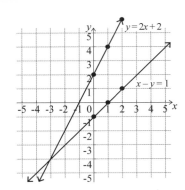

Solution is (2, 5).   Solution is (4, 0).   Solution is (−3, −4).

1. Complete each table of values and graph each line on the number plane provided:

(a) $y = x + 2$

x	0	1	2
y			

(b) $y = 2x - 1$

x	-1	0	1
y			

(c) $x + y = 0$

x	1	2	3
y			

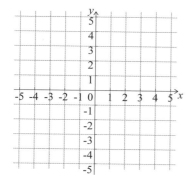

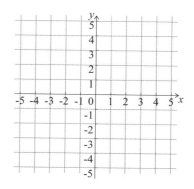

2. Graph each pair of equations on the same diagram and find the simultaneous solution:

(a) $y = x + 1$ and $y = -x - 3$

x	-1	0	1
y			

x	-1	0	1
y			

(b) $y = 2x - 3$ and $y = x - 3$

x	1	2	3
y			

x	1	2	3
y			

(c) $x - y = 4$ and $x + y = 2$

x	0	1	2
y			

x	0	1	2
y			

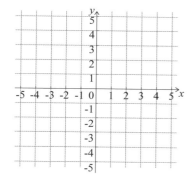

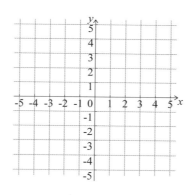

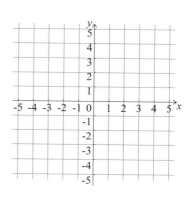

Solution is _____

Solution is _____

Solution is _____

(d) $y = 3x + 2$ and $y = x - 2$

x	-1	0	1
y			

x	-1	0	1
y			

(e) $y = -2x + 3$ and $y = x$

x	1	2	3
y			

x	1	2	3
y			

(f) $x + y + 2 = 0$ and $2x - y + 1 = 0$

x	0	1	2
y			

x	0	1	2
y			

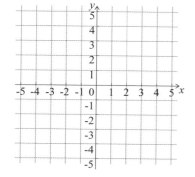

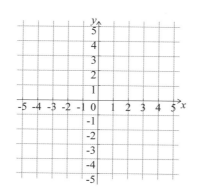

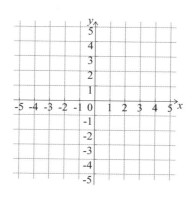

1. Complete each table of values and graph each line on the number plane provided:

   (a) $y = x + 2$

x	0	1	2
y	2	3	4

When $x = 0$, $y = 0 + 2$
               $= 2$

When $x = 1$, $y = 1 + 2$
               $= 3$

When $x = 2$, $y = 2 + 2$
               $= 4$

☞ Mark each of these three points, [(0, 2), (1, 3) and (2, 4)] on the grid.

☞ Draw the line going right through these three points, and across the grid. Don't just join the dots! (The points we have found using the table of values are just three examples of points that lie on the line. There is an infinite number of other points, all of which lie on the line.) Arrows at the 'ends' of the line show that it doesn't actually end but continues indefinitely. Always write the name of the line on the diagram.

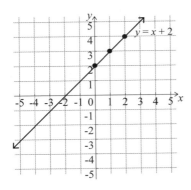

(b) $y = 2x - 1$

x	−1	0	1
y	−3	−1	1

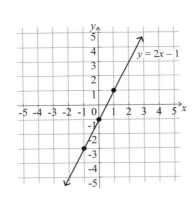

(c) $x + y = 0$

x	1	2	3
y	−1	−2	−3

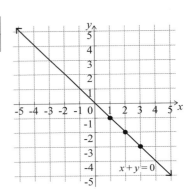

2. Graph each pair of equations on the same diagram and find the simultaneous solution:

(a) $y = x + 1$ and $y = -x - 3$

x	−1	0	1
y	0	1	2

x	−1	0	1
y	−2	−3	−4

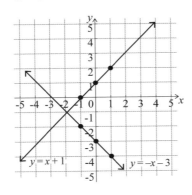

☞ Graph each of the lines in the same way as in question 1.
The two lines will have just one point of intersection.
The coordinates of this point give the simultaneous solution of the pair of equations.

Solution is (−2, −1).

☞ You could also write the solution as $x = -2$ and $y = -1$.

(b) $y = 2x - 3$ and $y = x - 3$

$y = 2x - 3$

x	1	2	3
y	–1	1	–3

$y = x - 3$

x	1	2	3
y	–2	–1	0

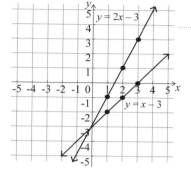

☞ The tables of values have been provided to help you draw the lines.
If you know a different method to determine where to draw the lines, you can use that instead.

Solution is (0, –3).

(c) $x - y = 4$ and $x + y = 2$

$x - y = 4$

x	0	1	2
y	–4	–3	–2

$x + y = 2$

x	0	1	2
y	2	1	0

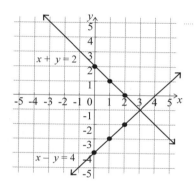

☞ You might find it easier to rearrange the equations before filling in the tables of values.
$x - y = 4$ is the same thing as $y = x - 4$.
$x + y = 2$ is the same as
$y = -x + 2$ (or $y = 2 - x$).

Solution is (3, –1).

(d) $y = 3x + 2$ and $y = x - 2$

$y = 3x + 2$			
x	–1	0	1
y	–1	2	5

$y = x - 2$			
x	–1	0	1
y	–3	–2	–1

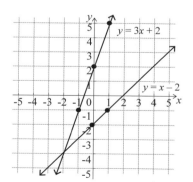

Solution is (–2, –4).

(e) $y = -2x + 3$ and $y = x$

$y = -2x + 3$			
x	1	2	3
y	1	–1	–3

$y = x$			
x	1	2	3
y	1	2	3

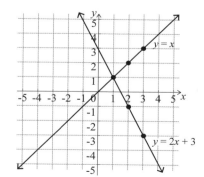

Solution is (1, 1).

(f) $x + y + 2 = 0$ and $2x - y + 1 = 0$

$x + y + 2 = 0$			
x	0	1	2
y	–2	–3	–4

$2x - y + 1 = 0$			
x	0	1	2
y	1	3	5

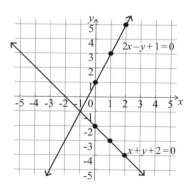

Solution is (–1, –1).

Finding the solution to many practical problems can be reduced to solving a pair of simultaneous equations. We can use any method (substitution, elimination or graphing) to solve these equations.

Example:
A factory produces two types of garments, shirts and dresses. It costs $2 to make a shirt and $3 to make a dress. How many of each garment did the factory produce on a day when 100 garments were made and costs totalled $225?

Solution:
Let s be the number of shirts and d be the number of dresses.

	$s + d = 100$	(i)
	$2s + 3d = 225$	(ii)
(i) $\times 2$:	$2s + 2d = 200$	(iii)
(ii) $-$ (iii):	$d = 25$	
Substitute in (i):	$s + 25 = 100$	
	$s = 75$	

100 garments (shirts plus dresses) are made.
Costs total $2 for each shirt and $3 for each dress.
We can eliminate either pronumeral.

$\therefore$ **75 shirts and 25 dresses were made on that day.**

We must take care to answer the question that is asked.

Example:
5 apples and 3 bananas cost $3.90 and at the same time 7 apples and 2 bananas cost $4.25. How much is each apple?

Solution:
Let a be the price of an apple and b be the price of a banana.

	$5a + 3b = \$3.90$	(i)
	$7a + 2b = \$4.25$	(ii)
(i) $\times 2$:	$10a + 6b = \$7.80$	(iii)
(ii) $\times 3$:	$21a + 6b = \$12.75$	(iv)
(iv) $-$ (iii):	$11a = \$4.95$	
	$a = \$0.45$	

Note: We don't need to find the price of a banana.

$\therefore$ **the price of each apple is 45 cents.**

Example:
Molly and her grandmother share the same birthday. On their last birthday their combined ages totalled 97 years, and Molly's grandmother was 5 years more than 3 times Molly's age. How old will they be on their next birthday?

Solution:
Let Molly's age be m years, and her grandmother's age be g years.

	$m + g = 97$	(i)
	$g = 3m + 5$	(ii)
Substitute (ii) into (i):	$m + (3m + 5) = 97$	
	$4m + 5 = 97$	
	$4m = 92$	
	$m = 23$	
Substitute into (ii):	$g = 3 \times 23 + 5$	
	$= 74$	

$\therefore$ Molly is 23 and her grandmother is 74.
On their next birthday, Molly will turn 24 and her grandmother will be 75 years old.

1. Form a pair of simultaneous equations and solve them to answer these problems:

(a) Gordana and Kate together invested $2000 in a new business. If Gordana invested 3 times as much as Kate, how much did each invest?

(b) Stephen scored 224 runs in a cricket match. In the second innings he scored 8 more runs than he scored in the first innings. How many runs did Stephen score in each innings?

(c) 3 books and 7 pencils cost $10.40, while 8 books and 5 pencils cost $14.75. How much is each pencil?

(d) There are both sheep and emus in a paddock. Altogether there are 94 heads and 300 legs. How many sheep are in the paddock?

(e) Alice is 17 years older than her brother. Their combined ages total 41 years. How old are Alice and her brother?

(f) 10 bolts and 8 nuts weigh 372 grams, while 6 bolts and 13 nuts weigh 297 grams. What would be the combined weight of 7 bolts and 10 nuts?

SIMULTANEOUS EQUATIONS Worked Solutions

1. Form a pair of simultaneous equations and solve them to answer these problems:

    (a) Gordana and Kate together invested $2000 in a new business. If Gordana invested 3 times as much as Kate, how much did each invest?

    Let g be the amount invested by Gordana .... ☞ Begin with a statement like this.
    and k be the amount invested by Kate.

    $$g + k = 2000 \quad \text{(i)}$$ ☞ The total of their investments was $2000.
    $$g = 3k \quad \text{(ii)}$$ ☞ Gordana invested 3 times as much as Kate.

    Substitute (ii) into (i): $3k + k = 2000$ ☞ Solve this new equation.
    $$4k = 2000$$
    $$k = 500$$

    Substitute into (ii): $g = 3 \times 500$
    $$g = 1500$$

    ∴ **Gordana invests $1500 and Kate invests $500.** ☞ Give the answer in a sentence.

    (b) Stephen scored 224 runs in a cricket match. In the second innings he scored 8 more runs than he scored in the first innings. How many runs did Stephen score in each innings?

    Let a be the number of runs Stephen scored in the .... ☞ Begin with a statement like this.
    1st innings and b be the number of runs in the 2nd.

    $$a + b = 224 \quad \text{(i)}$$ ☞ Stephen scored 224 runs in the match.
    $$b = a + 8 \quad \text{(ii)}$$ ☞ He scored 8 runs more in the 2nd innings.

    Substitute (ii) into (i): $a + (a + 8) = 224$
    $$2a + 8 = 224$$
    $$2a = 216$$
    $$a = 108$$

    Substitute into (ii) $b = 108 + 8$
    $$b = 116$$

    ∴ **Stephen scored 108 runs in the first innings** .... ☞ Check that the solution satisfies the question.
    and 116 runs in the second innings.

    (c) 3 books and 7 pencils cost $10.40, while 8 books and 5 pencils cost $14.75. How much is each pencil?

    Let b be the cost of a book and p the cost of a pencil. .... ☞ Begin with a statement like this.
    You can use any pronumerals.
    $$3b + 7p = \$10.40 \quad \text{(i)}$$
    $$8b + 5p = \$14.75 \quad \text{(ii)}$$
    (i) × 8: $24b + 56p = \$83.20 \quad \text{(iii)}$ ☞ Because we only need to find the
    (ii) × 3: $24b + 15p = \$44.25 \quad \text{(iv)}$ price of a pencil, we eliminate b.
    (iii) − (iv): $41p = \$38.95$
    $$p = \$0.95$$

    ∴ **the cost of each pencil is 95 cents.** .... ☞ Answer the question that is asked.

(d) There are both sheep and emus in a paddock.
Altogether there are 94 heads and 300 legs.
How many sheep are in the paddock?

Let s be the number of sheep and e the number of emus.

$$s + e = 94 \quad \text{(i)}$$ ☞ There are 94 heads, so 94 animals.
$$4s + 2e = 300 \quad \text{(ii)}$$ Each sheep has 4 legs and each emu 2.
(i) × 2: $\quad 2s + 2e = 188 \quad \text{(iii)}$ ☞ Or we could divide equation (ii) by 2.
(ii) − (iii): $\quad\quad 2s = 112$
$$s = 56$$
Substitute into (i): $\quad 56 + e = 94$
$$e = 38$$ ☞ Check the solution in equation (ii).
∴ **there are 56 sheep and 38 emus in the paddock.** Write the answer in a sentence.

(e) Alice is 17 years older than her brother. Their
combined ages total 41 years. How old are Alice
and her brother?

Let Alice's age be a years and her brother's age be b.

$$a = b + 17 \quad \text{(i)}$$ ☞ Alice is 17 years older than her brother.
$$a + b = 41 \quad \text{(ii)}$$ ☞ Their combined ages total 41.
Substitute (i) into (ii): $\quad (b + 17) + b = 41$
$$2b + 17 = 41$$
$$2b = 24$$
$$b = 12$$
Substitute into (i): $\quad a = 12 + 17$
$$a = 29$$
∴ **Alice is 29 years old and her brother is 12.** ☞ Answer with a statement.

(f) 10 bolts and 8 nuts weigh 372 grams, while 6 bolts
and 13 nuts weigh 297 grams. What would be the
combined weight of 7 bolts and 10 nuts?

Let b be the weight of a bolt and n the weight of a nut. ☞ Begin with a statement like this.
$$10b + 8n = 372 \quad \text{(i)}$$ 10 bolts and 8 nuts weigh 372 grams.
$$6b + 13n = 297 \quad \text{(ii)}$$ 6 bolts and 13 nuts weigh 297 grams.
(i) × 3: $\quad 30b + 24n = 1116 \quad \text{(iii)}$ ☞ We could eliminate n instead.
(ii) × 5: $\quad 30b + 65n = 1485 \quad \text{(iv)}$
(iv) − (iii): $\quad\quad 41n = 369$
$$n = 9$$
Substitute into (i): $\quad 10b + 8 \times 9 = 372$
$$10b + 72 = 372$$
$$10b = 300$$
$$b = 30$$
∴ **a bolt weighs 30 grams and a nut weighs 9 grams.**
The weight of 7 bolts and 10 nuts $= 7 \times 30 + 10 \times 9$ ☞ Make sure you answer the question
$$= 300 \text{ grams.}$$ that is asked.

REVIEW OF FACTORISATION Summary

> *Remember:*
> We can always check our factorisation by e-x-p-a-n-d-i-n-g.

When factorising we write an expression as a product of its factors. There are several different types of factorising.

Common factors:
Look for the largest number, or term, that divides evenly into each part of the expression.

Example:
Factorise: (a) $12x - 18$ (b) $m^2 + m$ (c) $15ab - 20b^2 + 25b$ (d) $9a^2b^3 - 6ab^5$

Solution:
(a) $12x - 18 = 6(2x - 3)$
(c) $15ab - 20b^2 + 25b = 5b(3a - 4b + 5)$
(b) $m^2 + m = m(m + 1)$
(d) $9a^2b^3 - 6ab^5 = 3ab^3(3a - 2b^2)$

Factorising by grouping:
By grouping terms together we can sometimes find a common factor.

Example:
Factorise:
(a) $x^2 + 5x + xy + 5y$ (b) $8p - 6q - 4pq + 3q^2$ (c) $m^2 + mn - m - n$

Solution:
(a) $x^2 + 5x + xy + 5y$
  $= x(x + 5) + y(x + 5)$
  $= (x + 5)(x + y)$

(b) $8p - 6q - 4pq + 3q^2$
  $= 2(4p - 3q) - q(4p - 3q)$
  $= (4p - 3q)(2 - q)$

(c) $m^2 + mn - m - n$
  $= m(m + n) - 1(m + n)$
  $= (m + n)(m - 1)$

Difference of two squares:
$$a^2 - b^2 = (a + b)(a - b)$$

Example:
Factorise: (a) $x^2 - 64$ (b) $y^2 - 1$ (c) $9p^2 - 25q^2$ (d) $a^4 - 16b^2$

Solution:
(a) $x^2 - 64 = x^2 - 8^2$
           $= (x + 8)(x - 8)$

(b) $y^2 - 1 = y^2 - 1^2$
        $= (y + 1)(y - 1)$

(c) $9p^2 - 25q^2 = (3p)^2 - (5q)^2$
              $= (3p + 5q)(3p - 5q)$

(d) $a^4 - 16b^2 = (a^2)^2 - (4b)^2$
             $= (a^2 + 4b)(a^2 - 4b)$

Trinomials:
Look for two numbers that multiply to the last term and add to give the coefficient of the middle term.
$$x^2 + (a + b)x + ab = (x + a)(x + b)$$

Example:
Factorise: (a) $x^2 + 9x + 20$ (b) $m^2 - 3m - 10$ (c) $p^2 - 12p + 32$ (d) $a^2 + 7a - 18$

Solution:
(a) $x^2 + 9x + 20 = (x + 5)(x + 4)$ (What 2 numbers multiply to 20 and add to 9?)
(b) $m^2 - 3m - 10 = (m - 5)(m + 2)$ (What 2 numbers multiply to −10 and add to −3?)
(c) $p^2 - 12p + 32 = (p - 8)(p - 4)$ (What 2 numbers multiply to 32 and add to −12?)
(d) $a^2 + 7a - 18 = (a + 9)(a - 2)$ (What 2 numbers multiply to −18 and add to 7?)

1. **Factorise by taking out a common factor:**

   (a) $15e - 10$ = _____

   (b) $t^2 + 3t$ = _____

   (c) $e^2 - e$ = _____

   (d) $16ab - 24a + 20b$ = _____

   (e) $9p^2 - 3p^5$ = _____

   (f) $12x^4y^3 + 8x^2y^4$ = _____

2. **Factorise by grouping:**

   (a) $a^2 + 8a + ab + 8b$ = _____

   = _____

   (b) $x^2 - 7x + xy - 7y$ = _____

   = _____

   (c) $p^2 - pq + p - q$ = _____

   = _____

   (d) $10g - 5h - 2gh + h^2$ = _____

   = _____

   (e) $6ab - 15ac + 8b^2 - 20bc$

   = _____

   = _____

   (f) $c^2 + 2c - c - 2$

   = _____

   = _____

3. **Factorise each difference of two squares:**

   (a) $x^2 - 36$ = _____

   = _____

   (b) $a^2 - 1$ = _____

   = _____

   (c) $4p^2 - q^2$ = _____

   = _____

   (d) $81 - e^2$ = _____

   = _____

   (e) $100m^2 - 49n^2$ = _____

   = _____

   (f) $x^4 - 144y^2$ = _____

   = _____

4. **Factorise each trinomial:**

   (a) $x^2 + 8x - 33$ = _____

   (b) $t^2 - 5t + 6$ = _____

   (c) $q^2 + 4q - 21$ = _____

   (d) $h^2 - 2h - 63$ = _____

   (e) $a^2 + a - 30$ = _____

   (f) $k^2 - 16k + 64$ = _____

5. **Factorise:**

   (a) $t^2 - 9t + 18$ = _____

   (b) $t^2 - 9t$ = _____

   (c) $t^2 - 9$ = _____

   = _____

   (d) $t^2 - 9t - tu + 9u$ = _____

   = _____

6. **Factorise fully (first take out a common factor):**

   (a) $3u^2 - 12$ = _____

   = _____

   (b) $2x^2 - 16x + 30$ = _____

   = _____

1. Factorise, by taking out a common factor:

   (a) $15e - 10 = \mathbf{5(3e - 2)}$ .... ☞ What divides into both $15e$ and 10?

   (b) $t^2 + 3t = \mathbf{t(t + 3)}$ .... ☞ What divides into both t^2 and $3t$?

   (c) $e^2 - e = \mathbf{e(e - 1)}$ .... ☞ Don't forget the one.

   (d) $16ab - 24a + 20b = \mathbf{4(4ab - 6a + 5b)}$ .... ☞ 2 is a common factor but the largest common factor of all three terms is 4.

   (e) $9p^2 - 3p^5 = \mathbf{3p^2(3 - p^3)}$ .... ☞ Always take out the largest common factor.

   (f) $12x^4y^3 + 8x^2y^4 = \mathbf{4x^2y^3(3x^2 + 2y)}$ .... ☞ Check by expanding the answer.

2. Factorise by grouping:

   (a) $a^2 + 8a + ab + 8b = \mathbf{a(a + 8) + b(a + 8)}$ .... ☞ Group in pairs to find common factors.
   $= \mathbf{(a + 8)(a + b)}$ The new common factor is $(a + 8)$.

   (b) $x^2 - 7x + xy - 7y = \mathbf{x(x - 7) + y(x - 7)}$
   $= \mathbf{(x - 7)(x + y)}$

   (c) $p^2 - pq + p - q = \mathbf{p(p - q) + 1(p - q)}$ .... ☞ It is not necessary to write the 1 in this line, but it must not be left out in this line.
   $= \mathbf{(p - q)(p + 1)}$

   (d) $10g - 5h - 2gh + h^2 = \mathbf{5(2g - h) - h(2g - h)}$ .... ☞ Be careful with the signs.
   $= \mathbf{(2g - h)(5 - h)}$

   (e) $6ab - 15ac + 8b^2 - 20bc = \mathbf{3a(2b - 5c) + 4b(2b - 5c)}$
   $= \mathbf{(2b - 5c)(3a + 4b)}$

   (f) $c^2 + 2c - c - 2 = \mathbf{c(c + 2) - 1(c + 2)}$
   $= \mathbf{(c + 2)(c - 1)}$

3. Factorise each difference of two squares:

   (a) $x^2 - 36 = \mathbf{x^2 - 6^2}$ .... ☞ First express as two squares.
   $= \mathbf{(x + 6)(x - 6)}$

   (b) $a^2 - 1 = \mathbf{a^2 - 1^2}$
   $= \mathbf{(a + 1)(a - 1)}$

   (c) $4p^2 - q^2 = \mathbf{(2p)^2 - q^2}$ .... ☞ $4p^2 = 2^2 \times p^2 = (2p)^2$
   $= \mathbf{(2p + q)(2p - q)}$

(d) $81 - e^2 = \mathbf{9^2 - e^2}$
$= \mathbf{(9 + e)(9 - e)}$ ☞ $(e + 9)(e - 9)$ is NOT the same thing.

(e) $100m^2 - 49n^2 = \mathbf{(10m)^2 - (7n)^2}$
$= \mathbf{(10m + 7n)(10m - 7n)}$

(f) $x^4 - 144y^2 = \mathbf{(x^2)^2 - (12y)^2}$ ☞ Remember: $x^2 \times x^2 = x^4$
$= \mathbf{(x^2 + 12y)(x^2 - 12y)}$

4. Factorise each trinomial:

(a) $x^2 + 8x - 33 = \mathbf{(x + 11)(x - 3)}$ ☞ What 2 numbers add to 8 and multiply to –33?
$(x - 3)(x + 11)$ is the same thing.

(b) $t^2 - 5t + 6 = \mathbf{(t - 3)(t - 2)}$ ☞ What 2 numbers add to –5 and multiply to 6?

(c) $q^2 + 4q - 21 = \mathbf{(q + 7)(q - 3)}$ ☞ What 2 numbers add to 4 and multiply to –21?

(d) $h^2 - 2h - 63 = \mathbf{(h - 9)(h + 7)}$ ☞ $(h + 7)(h - 9)$ is the same thing.

(e) $a^2 + a - 30 = \mathbf{(a + 6)(a - 5)}$ ☞ What 2 numbers add to 1 and multiply to –30?

(f) $k^2 - 16k + 64 = \mathbf{(k - 8)(k - 8)}$ ☞ or $(k - 8)^2$

5. Factorise:

(a) $t^2 - 9t + 18 = \mathbf{(t - 6)(t - 3)}$ ☞ What 2 numbers add to –9 and multiply to 18?

(b) $t^2 - 9t = \mathbf{t(t - 9)}$ ☞ t is the common factor.

(c) $t^2 - 9 = \mathbf{t^2 - 3^2}$ ☞ This is a difference of two squares.
$= \mathbf{(t + 3)(t - 3)}$

(d) $t^2 - 9t - tu + 9u = \mathbf{t(t - 9) - u(t - 9)}$ ☞ Factorise by grouping in pairs.
$= \mathbf{(t - 9)(t - u)}$

6. Factorise fully (first take out the common factor):

(a) $3u^2 - 12 = \mathbf{3(u^2 - 4)}$ ☞ First take out the common factor. In the
$= \mathbf{3(u^2 - 2^2)}$ brackets we now have a difference of 2 squares.
$= \mathbf{3(u + 2)(u - 2)}$ Don't leave out the three.

(b) $2x^2 - 16x + 30 = \mathbf{2(x^2 - 8x + 15)}$ ☞ First take out the common factor.
$= \mathbf{2(x - 5)(x - 3)}$ Then factorise the trinomial.

Trinomials such as $3x^2 + 11x + 8$ are not so easy to factorise. There are a few different methods of factorising this type of trinomial, but we are only looking at one here—the cross method. By drawing a cross and writing down the different combinations, we have a trial and error method of factorising.

To factorise $3x^2 + 11x + 8$, these are the steps we might take:

1. Draw a cross.
2. On the left side, write down a pair of terms that multiply to the first term of the trinomial.
3. On the right side, write down a pair of numbers that multiply to the last term of the trinomial.
4. Multiply along the arms of the cross.
5. Check to see if these products add up to the middle term of the trinomial.
6. When you have the right combination, write down the solution.

This is found by reading across the top and across the bottom of the cross.

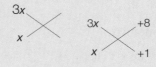

$3x \times 1 + x \times 8$

$3x + 8x = 11x$ ✓

$3x^2 + 11x + 8 = (3x + 8)(x + 1)$

Example:
Factorise $3x^2 + 14x + 8$

Solution:
$3x^2 + 14x + 8 = (3x + 2)(x + 4)$ (using the diagrams below).

$3x \times 1 + x \times 8 = 11x$ ✗ $3x \times 8 + x \times 1 = 25x$ ✗ $3x \times 2 + x \times 4 = 10x$ ✗ $3x \times 4 + x \times 2 = 14x$ ✓

Example:
Factorise $4x^2 + 8x + 3$

> There may be different possible combinations of terms for the first term as well as for the last term.

Solution:
$4x^2 + 8x + 3 = (2x + 3)(2x + 1)$

$4x \times 1 + x \times 3 = 7x$ ✗ $4x \times 3 + x \times 1 = 13x$ ✗ $2x \times 1 + 2x \times 3 = 8x$ ✓

Example:
Factorise: (a) $5x^2 + 31x + 6$ (b) $7x^2 + 31x + 12$

> It is not necessary to find every possible combination. We just need to find the solution.

Solution:
(a) $5x^2 + 31x + 6 = (5x + 1)(x + 6)$ (b) $7x^2 + 31x + 12 = (7x + 3)(x + 4)$

$5x \times 6 + x \times 1 = 31x$ ✓ $7x \times 4 + x \times 3 = 31x$ ✓

1. Use the cross method to factorise these trinomials. (3 crosses have been provided for each question. You might not need all these, or you might need to draw more before you find the right combination. Alternatively, you might use a different method to factorise these trinomials.) [No negatives have been used in these questions.]

(a) $2x^2 + 11x + 15$ = _____

(b) $3x^2 + 13x + 4$ = _____

(c) $7x^2 + 37x + 10$ = _____

(d) $5x^2 + 21x + 18$ = _____

(e) $11x^2 + 80x + 21$ = _____

(f) $2x^2 + 11x + 12$ = _____

(g) $4x^2 + 16x + 7$ = _____

(h) $6x^2 + 11x + 5$ = _____

(i) $6x^2 + 19x + 10$ = _____

(j) $4x^2 + 15x + 9$ = _____

(k) $10x^2 + 21x + 8$ = _____

(l) $9x^2 + 18x + 8$ = _____

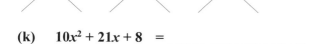

(m) $12x^2 + 7x + 1$ = _____

(n) $12x^2 + 28x + 15$ = _____

1. Use the cross method to factorise these trinomials.

   (a) $2x^2 + 11x + 15$

   $2x^2 + 11x + 15 = (2x + 5)(x + 3)$

   ☞ On the left-hand side of the cross, the terms multiply to $2x^2$. They can only be $2x$ and x. On the right-hand side the two numbers multiply to 15. They could be 15 and 1, or 5 and 3 in some order.
   Using the crosses and multiplying along the arms, only one combination gives a sum of $11x$.

   $2x \times 1 + x \times 15 = 17x$ ✗ $2x \times 15 + x \times 1 = 31x$ ✗

   ☞ The solution is $(2x + 5)(x + 3)$, reading across the top and bottom of the cross that gives the right combination.

   $2x \times 3 + x \times 5 = 11x$ ✓ $2x \times 5 + x \times 3 = 13x$ ✗

   There is no need to swap the terms on the left-hand side of the cross.

   This is because  is exactly the same as

   $x \times 5 + 2x \times 3 = 11x$ $2x \times 3 + x \times 5 = 11x$

   $2x^2 + 11x + 15 = (x + 3)(2x + 5)$ is the same thing as $2x^2 + 11x + 15 = (2x + 5)(x + 3)$.

   (b) $3x^2 + 13x + 4$

   ☞ The terms on the left-hand side multiply to $3x^2$, the numbers on the right-hand side multiply to 4.

   $3x \times 2 + x \times 2 = 8x$ ✗ $3x \times 1 + x \times 4 = 7x$ ✗

   $3x \times 4 + x \times 1 = 13x$ ✓
   $3x^2 + 13x + 4 = (3x + 1)(x + 4)$

   There is no need to look for every combination. You only need to look for the **right** combination.

   (c) $7x^2 + 37x + 10 = (7x + 2)(x + 5)$ (d) $5x^2 + 21x + 18 = (5x + 6)(x + 3)$

   $7x \times 5 + x \times 2 = 37x$ ✓ $5x \times 3 + x \times 6 = 21x$ ✓

(e) $11x^2 + 80x + 21 = (\mathbf{11x + 3})(\mathbf{x + 7})$

$$11x \quad \diagdown \quad +3$$
$$x \quad \diagup \quad +7$$

$11x \times 7 + x \times 3 = 80x$ ✓

(f) $2x^2 + 11x + 12 = (\mathbf{2x + 3})(\mathbf{x + 4})$

$$2x \quad \diagdown \quad +3$$
$$x \quad \diagup \quad +4$$

$2x \times 4 + x \times 3 = 11x$ ✓

(g) $4x^2 + 16x + 7 = (\mathbf{2x + 7})(\mathbf{2x + 1})$ ☞ There can also be different possible combinations for the left-hand side of the cross.

$$4x \quad \diagdown \quad +7$$
$$x \quad \diagup \quad +1$$
$4x \times 1 + x \times 7 = 11x$ ✗

$$4x \quad \diagdown \quad +1$$
$$x \quad \diagup \quad +7$$
$4x \times 7 + x \times 1 = 29x$ ✗

$$2x \quad \diagdown \quad +7$$
$$2x \quad \diagup \quad +1$$
$2x \times 1 + 2x \times 7 = 16x$ ✓

(h) $6x^2 + 11x + 5 = (\mathbf{6x + 5})(\mathbf{x + 1})$ ☞ *Remember*: The answer is found by reading across the top and across the bottom of the cross.

$$6x \quad \diagdown \quad +5$$
$$x \quad \diagup \quad +1$$

$6x \times 1 + x \times 5 = 11x$ ✓

(i) $6x^2 + 19x + 10 = (\mathbf{3x + 2})(\mathbf{2x + 5})$

$$3x \quad \diagdown \quad +2$$
$$2x \quad \diagup \quad +5$$

$3x \times 5 + 2x \times 2 = 19x$ ✓

(j) $4x^2 + 15x + 9 = (\mathbf{4x + 3})(\mathbf{x + 3})$

$$4x \quad \diagdown \quad +3$$
$$x \quad \diagup \quad +3$$

$4x \times 3 + x \times 3 = 15x$ ✓

(k) $10x^2 + 21x + 8 = (\mathbf{5x + 8})(\mathbf{2x + 1})$

$$5x \quad \diagdown \quad +8$$
$$2x \quad \diagup \quad +1$$

$5x \times 1 + 2x \times 8 = 21x$ ✓

(l) $9x^2 + 18x + 8 = (\mathbf{3x + 4})(\mathbf{3x + 2})$

$$3x \quad \diagdown \quad +4$$
$$3x \quad \diagup \quad +2$$

$3x \times 2 + 3x \times 4 = 18x$ ✓

(m) $12x^2 + 7x + 1 = (\mathbf{4x + 1})(\mathbf{3x + 1})$

$$4x \quad \diagdown \quad +1$$
$$3x \quad \diagup \quad +1$$

$4x \times 1 + 3x \times 1 = 7x$ ✓

(n) $12x^2 + 28x + 15 = (\mathbf{6x + 5})(\mathbf{2x + 3})$

$$6x \quad \diagdown \quad +5$$
$$2x \quad \diagup \quad +3$$

$6x \times 3 + 2x \times 5 = 28x$ ✓

Consider $5x^2 + 13x - 6$. In this case we need to look for two numbers that multiply to –6. Because the two numbers multiply to a negative number, we know that one is positive and one is negative.

Example:
Factorise $5x^2 + 13x - 6$

Solution:
$5x^2 + 13x - 6 = (5x - 2)(x + 3)$ (After considering the following combinations:)

$5x \times -1 + x \times 6 = x$ ✗ $5x \times 1 + x \times -6 = -x$ ✗ $5x \times -6 + x \times 1 = -29x$ ✗ $5x \times 6 + x \times -1 = 29x$ ✗

$5x \times -2 + x \times 3 = -7x$ ✗ $5x \times 2 + x \times -3 = 7x$ ✗ $5x \times -3 + x \times 2 = -13x$ ✗ $5x \times 3 + x \times -2 = 13x$ ✓

Note that changing the signs on the numbers on the cross also changes the sign of the sum. So, because the first combination in the above example didn't work, (= x), we know that the second combination would add to –x and so wouldn't be correct either. We wouldn't need to try that combination!

Consider $3x^2 - 20x + 12$.
The numbers multiply to 12, but the sum of our products is –20x.
Both numbers must therefore be negative.

Example:
Factorise $3x^2 - 20x + 12$

Solution:
$3x^2 - 20x + 12 = (3x - 2)(x - 6)$

$3x \times -1 + x \times -12 = -15x$ ✗ $3x \times -2 + x \times -6 = -12x$ ✗

$3x \times -12 + x \times -1 = -37x$ ✗ $3x \times -6 + x \times -2 = -20x$ ✓

Don't get cross!
Use these tips:
- Always check for a common factor first.
- If the last term is negative the signs must be different.
- If both the last term and the middle term are positive, both signs must be positive.
- If the last term is positive but the middle term is negative, both signs must be negative.
- If you have the 'right' sum but with the wrong sign, swap the signs on the cross.

1. **Use the cross method to factorise these trinomials.**
   (3 crosses have been provided for each question. You might not need all of them or you might need to draw more before you find the right combination.)

(a) $2x^2 + x - 6$ = _____

(b) $5x^2 - 19x - 4$ = _____

(c) $3x^2 - 17x + 10$ = _____

(d) $7x^2 + 41x - 6$ = _____

(e) $2x^2 - 9x + 10$ = _____

(f) $9x^2 + 21x + 10$ = _____

(g) $4x^2 - 8x + 3$ = _____

(h) $4x^2 - x - 14$ = _____

(i) $10x^2 - 31x + 15$ = _____

(j) $6x^2 - 19x - 20$ = _____

(k) $6x^2 + 13x + 6$ = _____

(l) $8x^2 + 18x - 35$ = _____

(m) $12x^2 + x - 1$ = _____

(n) $15x^2 - 22x + 8$ = _____

HARDER FACTORISING—CROSS METHOD Worked Solutions

1. Use the cross method to factorise these trinomials.

(a) $2x^2 + x - 6 = (2x - 3)(x + 2)$ .... ☞ The front terms multiply to $2x^2$. They can only be $2x$ and x. The last two terms multiply to -6, so they have different signs.

$2x \times 2 + x \times -3 = x$ ✓

There are several possibilities: -6 and 1, 6 and -1, -1 and 6, 1 and -6, -3 and 2, 3 and -2, -2 and 3, or 2 and -3.
We use the cross to find the only combination of terms that multiply to -6 and add to 1.

(b) $5x^2 - 19x - 4 = (5x + 1)(x - 4)$ .... ☞ The front terms multiply to $5x^2$. The last terms multiply to -4 and we need a combination that adds to $-19x$.

$5x \times -4 + x \times 1 = -19x$ ✓

(c) $3x^2 - 17x + 10 = (3x - 2)(x - 5)$ .... ☞ The first terms multiply to $3x^2$. The last terms multiply to 10, so they must have the same sign. The sum of the right combination is $-17x$.

$3x \times -5 + x \times -2 = -17x$ ✓

(d) $7x^2 + 41x - 6 = (7x - 1)(x + 6)$ .... ☞ *Remember*: The answer is found by reading across the top and across the bottom of the cross.

$7x \times 6 + x \times -1 = 41x$ ✓

(e) $2x^2 - 9x + 10 = (2x - 5)(x - 2)$ .... ☞ $(x - 2)(2x - 5)$ is the same thing. The factors can appear in any order.

$2x \times -2 + x \times -5 = -9x$ ✓

(f) $9x^2 + 21x + 10 = (3x + 5)(3x + 2)$ ....   The first terms multiply to $9x^2$. There are two possibilities. The two terms could be $9x$ and x or they could be $3x$ and $3x$.

We must find the combination that, along with the last numbers that must multiply to 10, gives a sum of $21x$.

$3x$ $+5$

$3x$ $+2$

$3x \times 2 + 3x \times 5 = 21x$ ✓

(g) $4x^2 - 8x + 3 = (2x - 3)(2x - 1)$

$2x$ -3

$2x$ -1

$2x \times -1 + 2x \times -3 = -8x$ ✓

(h) $4x^2 - x - 14 = (4x + 7)(x - 2)$

$4x$ $+7$

x -2

$4x \times -2 + x \times 7 = -x$ ✓

(i) $10x^2 - 31x + 15 = (5x - 3)(2x - 5)$

$5x$ -3

$2x$ -5

$5x \times -5 + 2x \times -3 = -31x$ ✓

(j) $6x^2 - 19x - 20 = (6x + 5)(x - 4)$

$6x$ $+5$

x -4

$6x \times -4 + x \times 5 = -19x$ ✓

(k) $6x^2 + 13x + 6 = (3x + 2)(2x + 3)$

$3x$ $+2$

$2x$ $+3$

$3x \times 3 + 2x \times 2 = 13x$ ✓

(l) $8x^2 + 18x - 35 = (4x - 5)(2x + 7)$

$4x$ -5

$2x$ $+7$

$4x \times 7 + 2x \times -5 = 18x$ ✓

(m) $12x^2 + x - 1 = (4x - 1)(3x + 1)$

$4x$ -1

$3x$ $+1$

$4x \times 1 + 3x \times -1 = x$ ✓

(n) $15x^2 - 22x + 8 = (5x - 4)(3x - 2)$

$5x$ -4

$3x$ -2

$5x \times -2 + 3x \times -4 = -22x$ ✓

NUMBERS THAT MULTIPLY TO ZERO Summary

> If two or more numbers multiply to zero, one of the numbers must be zero.
> If $ab = 0$, either $a = 0$ or $b = 0$ or both.

Example:

Solve: (a) $x(x - 9) = 0$ (b) $a(a + 6) = 0$

  (c) $p(p - 7) = 0$ (d) $3m(m + 1) = 0$

Solution:

(a) $\quad\quad x(x - 9) = 0$

$\quad x = 0 \quad$ or $\quad x - 9 = 0$

$\quad x = 0 \quad\quad$ or $\quad\quad x = 9$

(b) $\quad\quad a(a + 6) = 0$

$\quad a = 0 \quad$ or $\quad a + 6 = 0$

$\quad a = 0 \quad\quad$ or $\quad\quad a = -6$

(c) $\quad\quad p(p - 7) = 0$

$\quad p = 0 \quad$ or $\quad p - 7 = 0$

$\quad p = 0 \quad\quad$ or $\quad\quad p = 7$

(d) $\quad\quad 3m(m + 1) = 0$

$\quad 3m = 0 \quad$ or $\quad m + 1 = 0$

$\quad m = 0 \quad\quad$ or $\quad\quad m = -1$

> We might need to solve 2 simple equations.

Example:

Solve: (a) $(x - 6)(x - 4) = 0$ (b) $(a - 9)(a + 5) = 0$

  (c) $(d + 3)(d - 3) = 0$ (d) $(n + 2)(n + 8) = 0$

Solution:

(a) $\quad\quad (x - 6)(x - 4) = 0$

$\quad x - 6 = 0 \quad$ or $\quad x - 4 = 0$

$\quad\quad x = 6 \quad\quad$ or $\quad\quad x = 4$

(b) $\quad\quad (a - 9)(a + 5) = 0$

$\quad a - 9 = 0 \quad$ or $\quad a + 5 = 0$

$\quad\quad a = 9 \quad\quad$ or $\quad\quad a = -5$

(c) $\quad\quad (d + 3)(d - 3) = 0$

$\quad d + 3 = 0 \quad$ or $\quad d - 3 = 0$

$\quad\quad d = -3 \quad$ or $\quad\quad d = 3$

(d) $\quad\quad (n + 2)(n + 8) = 0$

$\quad n + 2 = 0 \quad$ or $\quad n + 8 = 0$

$\quad\quad n = -2 \quad$ or $\quad\quad n = -8$

> One, or both, solutions might involve fractions.

Example:

Solve: (a) $(2x + 1)(x - 10) = 0$ (b) $(x + 11)(3x - 2) = 0$

  (c) $(2x - 5)(7x - 4) = 0$ (d) $(8x + 3)(9x + 1) = 0$

Solution:

(a) $\quad (2x + 1)(x - 10) = 0$

$2x + 1 = 0 \quad$ or $\quad x - 10 = 0$

$\quad\quad 2x = -1 \quad$ or $\quad x = 10$

$\quad\quad x = -\dfrac{1}{2} \quad$ or $\quad x = 10$

(b) $\quad (x + 11)(3x - 2) = 0$

$x + 11 = 0 \quad$ or $\quad 3x - 2 = 0$

$\quad\quad x = -11 \quad$ or $\quad 3x = 2$

$\quad\quad x = -11 \quad$ or $\quad x = \dfrac{2}{3}$

(c) $\quad (2x - 5)(7x - 4) = 0$

$2x - 5 = 0 \quad$ or $\quad 7x - 4 = 0$

$\quad\quad 2x = 5 \quad$ or $\quad\quad 7x = 4$

$\quad\quad x = 2\dfrac{1}{2} \quad$ or $\quad\quad x = \dfrac{4}{7}$

(d) $\quad (8x + 3)(9x + 1) = 0$

$8x + 3 = 0 \quad$ or $\quad 9x + 1 = 0$

$\quad\quad 8x = -3 \quad$ or $\quad\quad 9x = -1$

$\quad\quad x = -\dfrac{3}{8} \quad$ or $\quad\quad x = -\dfrac{1}{9}$

1. **Solve:**

   (a) $x(x - 4) = 0$

   (b) $a(a + 2) = 0$

   (c) $e(e - 1) = 0$

   (d) $5k(k + 3) = 0$

   (e) $2p(p - 7) = 0$

   (f) $8y(y + 1) = 0$

2. **Solve:**

   (a) $(x - 3)(x - 2) = 0$

   (b) $(t - 7)(t - 1) = 0$

   (c) $(a + 4)(a - 9) = 0$

   (d) $(b - 5)(b + 6) = 0$

   (e) $(h + 2)(h + 7) = 0$

   (f) $(u + 11)(u + 12) = 0$

   (g) $(k + 10)(k - 10) = 0$

   (h) $(g - 8)(2 - g) = 0$

   (i) $(5 - c)(4 + c) = 0$

3. **Solve:**

   (a) $(2x - 5)(x - 8) = 0$

   (b) $(3a - 1)(a - 4) = 0$

   (c) $(5p - 3)(p - 7) = 0$

   (d) $(4x - 1)(x + 9) = 0$

   (e) $(2q + 1)(q - 11) = 0$

   (f) $(3h + 2)(h + 8) = 0$

   (g) $(7k - 2)(2k - 1) = 0$

   (h) $(5d - 2)(3d + 2) = 0$

   (i) $(4e + 3)(3e + 4) = 0$

   (j) $(3m + 1)(3m - 1) = 0$

   (k) $(8n + 5)(3n + 7) = 0$

   (l) $9v(6v - 5) = 0$

1. Solve:

(a) $x(x - 4) = 0$ .... 👉 One of the terms in the product must be zero.

$x = 0$ or $x - 4 = 0$
$x = 0$ or $x = 4$

(b) $a(a + 2) = 0$
$a = 0$ or $a + 2 = 0$ .... 👉 We have a simple equation to solve.
$a = 0$ or $a = -2$

(c) $e(e - 1) = 0$
$e = 0$ or $e - 1 = 0$
$e = 0$ or $e = 1$

(d) $5k(k + 3) = 0$ .... 👉 One of the terms in the product must be zero.
$5k = 0$ or $k + 3 = 0$ We now have two simple equations to solve.
$k = 0$ or $k = -3$

(e) $2p(p - 7) = 0$
$2p = 0$ or $p - 7 = 0$
$p = 0$ or $p = 7$

(f) $8y(y + 1) = 0$
$8y = 0$ or $y + 1 = 0$
$y = 0$ or $y = -1$

2. Solve:

(a) $(x - 3)(x - 2) = 0$ .... 👉 One of the terms in the product must be zero.
$x - 3 = 0$ or $x - 2 = 0$
$x = 3$ or $x = 2$

(b) $(t - 7)(t - 1) = 0$
$t - 7 = 0$ or $t - 1 = 0$ .... 👉 Solve two simple equations.
$t = 7$ or $t = 1$

(c) $(a + 4)(a - 9) = 0$
$a + 4 = 0$ or $a - 9 = 0$
$a = -4$ or $a = 9$

(d) $(b - 5)(b + 6) = 0$
$b - 5 = 0$ or $b + 6 = 0$
$b = 5$ or $b = -6$

(e) $(h + 2)(h + 7) = 0$
$h + 2 = 0$ or $h + 7 = 0$ .... 👉 You can always check that you have the right
$h = -2$ or $h = -7$ solution by substitution into the original equation.

(f) $(u + 11)(u + 12) = 0$
$u + 11 = 0$ or $u + 12 = 0$
$u = -11$ or $u = -12$

(g) $\quad (k+10)(k-10)=0$
$k+10=0 \quad$ or $\quad k-10=0$
$k=-10 \quad$ or $\qquad k=10$

(h) $\quad (g-8)(2-g)=0$
$g-8=0 \quad$ or $\quad 2-g=0$
$g=8 \quad$ or $\qquad g=2$

(i) $\quad (5-c)(4+c)=0$
$5-c=0 \quad$ or $\quad 4+c=0$
$c=5 \quad$ or $\qquad c=-4$

3. Solve:

(a) $\quad (2x-5)(x-8)=0$ .... ☞ One of the terms in the product must be zero.
$2x-5=0 \quad$ or $\quad x-8=0$
$2x=5 \qquad$ or $\quad x=8$
$x=2\frac{1}{2} \qquad$ or $\quad x=8$ .... ☞ The solution might involve fractions.

(b) $\quad (3a-1)(a-4)=0$
$3a-1=0 \quad$ or $\quad a-4=0$
$3a=1 \qquad$ or $\quad a=4$
$a=\frac{1}{3} \qquad$ or $\quad a=4$

(c) $\quad (5p-3)(p-7)=0$
$5p-3=0 \quad$ or $\quad p-7=0$
$5p=3 \quad$ or $\qquad p=7$
$p=\frac{3}{5} \quad$ or $\qquad p=7$ .... ☞ Decimals could be used instead of fractions.

(d) $\quad (4x-1)(x+9)=0$
$4x-1=0 \quad$ or $\quad x+9=0$
$4x=1 \quad$ or $\qquad x=-9$
$x=\frac{1}{4} \quad$ or $\qquad x=-9$ .... ☞ OR: $x=0.25 \quad$ or $\quad x=-9$

(e) $\quad (2q+1)(q-11)=0$
$2q+1=0 \quad$ or $\quad q-11=0$
$2q=-1 \quad$ or $\qquad q=11$
$q=-\frac{1}{2} \quad$ or $\qquad q=11$ .... ☞ *Remember*: you can always check by substitution.

(f) $\quad (3h+2)(h+8)=0$
$3h+2=0 \quad$ or $\quad h+8=0$
$3h=-2 \qquad$ or $\quad h=-8$
$h=-\frac{2}{3} \qquad$ or $\quad h=-8$

(g) $\quad (7k-2)(2k-1)=0$
$7k-2=0 \quad$ or $\quad 2k-1=0$
$7k=2 \quad$ or $\qquad 2k=1$
$k=\frac{2}{7} \quad$ or $\qquad k=\frac{1}{2}$

(h) $\quad (5d-2)(3d+2)=0$
$5d-2=0 \quad$ or $\quad 3d+2=0$
$5d=2 \quad$ or $\qquad 3d=-2$
$d=\frac{2}{5} \quad$ or $\qquad d=-\frac{2}{3}$

(i) $\quad (4e+3)(3e+4)=0$
$4e+3=0 \quad$ or $\quad 3e+4=0$
$4e=-3 \quad$ or $\qquad 3e=-4$
$e=-\frac{3}{4} \quad$ or $\qquad e=-1\frac{1}{3}$

(j) $\quad (3m+1)(3m-1)=0$
$3m+1=0 \quad$ or $\quad 3m-1=0$
$3m=-1 \quad$ or $\quad 3m=1$
$m=-\frac{1}{3} \quad$ or $\quad m=\frac{1}{3}$

(k) $\quad (8n+5)(3n+7)=0$
$8n+5=0 \quad$ or $\quad 3n+7=0$
$8n=-5 \quad$ or $\qquad 3n=-7$
$n=-\frac{5}{8} \quad$ or $\qquad n=-2\frac{1}{3}$

(l) $\quad 9v(6v-5)=0$
$9v=0 \quad$ or $\quad 6v-5=0$
$v=0 \quad$ or $\qquad 6v=5$
$v=0 \quad$ or $\qquad v=\frac{5}{6}$

A quadratic equation is an equation that involves a term that is squared.
Taking out a common factor might help us to solve a quadratic equation.

Quadratic means 'square'.

Example:
Solve: (a) $x^2 - 5x = 0$ (b) $2x^2 + 8x = 0$ (c) $x^2 - x = 0$

Solution:

(a)
$$x^2 - 5x = 0$$
$$x(x - 5) = 0$$
$$x = 0 \quad \text{or} \quad x - 5 = 0$$
$$x = 0 \quad \text{or} \quad x = 5$$

(b)
$$2x^2 + 8x = 0$$
$$2x(x + 4) = 0$$
$$2x = 0 \quad \text{or} \quad x + 4 = 0$$
$$x = 0 \quad \text{or} \quad x = -4$$

(c)
$$x^2 - x = 0$$
$$x(x - 1) = 0$$
$$x = 0 \quad \text{or} \quad x - 1 = 0$$
$$x = 0 \quad \text{or} \quad x = 1$$

We can also solve quadratic equations by first factorising a trinomial.

Example:
Solve: (a) $x^2 + 7x + 12 = 0$ (b) $a^2 - 8a + 15 = 0$
           (c) $t^2 - 4t - 21 = 0$ (d) $p^2 + 5p - 36 = 0$

Solution:

(a)
$$x^2 + 7x + 12 = 0$$
$$(x + 4)(x + 3) = 0$$
$$x + 4 = 0 \quad \text{or} \quad x + 3 = 0$$
$$x = -4 \quad \text{or} \quad x = -3$$

(b)
$$a^2 - 8a + 15 = 0$$
$$(a - 5)(a - 3) = 0$$
$$a - 5 = 0 \quad \text{or} \quad a - 3 = 0$$
$$a = 5 \quad \text{or} \quad a = 3$$

(c)
$$t^2 - 4t - 21 = 0$$
$$(t - 7)(t + 3) = 0$$
$$t - 7 = 0 \quad \text{or} \quad t + 3 = 0$$
$$t = 7 \quad \text{or} \quad t = -3$$

(d)
$$p^2 + 5p - 36 = 0$$
$$(p + 9)(p - 4) = 0$$
$$p + 9 = 0 \quad \text{or} \quad p - 4 = 0$$
$$p = -9 \quad \text{or} \quad p = 4$$

We might need to use the cross method to factorise a trinomial.

Example:
Solve: (a) $2x^2 + 19x + 35 = 0$ (b) $3x^2 - 17x + 10 = 0$
           (c) $10x^2 - 13x - 3 = 0$ (d) $8x^2 - 42x + 27 = 0$

Solution:

(a)
$$2x^2 + 19x + 35 = 0$$
$$(2x + 5)(x + 7) = 0$$
$$2x + 5 = 0 \quad \text{or} \quad x + 7 = 0$$
$$2x = -5 \quad \text{or} \quad x = -7$$
$$x = -2\tfrac{1}{2} \quad \text{or} \quad x = -7$$

(b)
$$3x^2 - 17x + 10 = 0$$
$$(3x - 2)(x - 5) = 0$$
$$3x - 2 = 0 \quad \text{or} \quad x - 5 = 0$$
$$3x = 2 \quad \text{or} \quad x = 5$$
$$x = \tfrac{2}{3} \quad \text{or} \quad x = 5$$

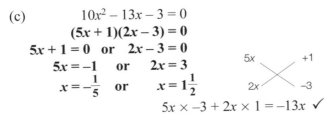

$2x \times 7 + x \times 5 = 19x$ ✓

$3x \times -5 + x \times -2 = -17x$ ✓

(c)
$$10x^2 - 13x - 3 = 0$$
$$(5x + 1)(2x - 3) = 0$$
$$5x + 1 = 0 \quad \text{or} \quad 2x - 3 = 0$$
$$5x = -1 \quad \text{or} \quad 2x = 3$$
$$x = -\tfrac{1}{5} \quad \text{or} \quad x = 1\tfrac{1}{2}$$

(d)
$$8x^2 - 42x + 27 = 0$$
$$(4x - 3)(2x - 9) = 0$$
$$4x - 3 = 0 \quad \text{or} \quad 2x - 9 = 0$$
$$4x = 3 \quad \text{or} \quad 2x = 9$$
$$x = \tfrac{3}{4} \quad \text{or} \quad x = 4\tfrac{1}{2}$$

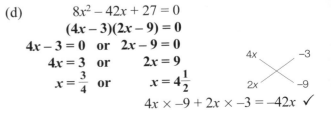

$5x \times -3 + 2x \times 1 = -13x$ ✓

$4x \times -9 + 2x \times -3 = -42x$ ✓

1. **Solve:**

   (a) $x^2 - 4x = 0$

   (b) $t^2 - 5t = 0$

   (c) $g^2 + 6g = 0$

   (d) $z^2 + z = 0$

   (e) $3m^2 - 6m = 0$

   (f) $7b^2 + 28b = 0$

   (g) $4a^2 - 6a = 0$

   (h) $9h^2 + 3h = 0$

   (i) $8n^2 - 10n = 0$

2. **Solve, by first factorising a trinomial:**

   (a) $x^2 + 9x + 14 = 0$

   (b) $e^2 - 13e + 40 = 0$

   (c) $p^2 - 5p - 24 = 0$

   (d) $n^2 - 2n - 35 = 0$

   (e) $k^2 + 10k + 16 = 0$

   (f) $d^2 - d - 30 = 0$

   (g) $s^2 + 4s - 12 = 0$

   (h) $u^2 - 9u + 20 = 0$

   (i) $m^2 + 3m - 18 = 0$

3. **Solve (you might need to use the cross method to factorise):**

   (a) $2x^2 + 7x + 3 = 0$

   (b) $5x^2 - 27x + 10 = 0$

   (c) $3x^2 + 16x - 12 = 0$

   (d) $8x^2 + 6x - 9 = 0$

1. Solve:

   (a)
$$x^2 - 4x = 0$$
$$x(x - 4) = 0$$
    ☞ Factorise first: x is a common factor.
$$x = 0 \quad \text{or} \quad x - 4 = 0$$
    One of the terms in the product must be zero.
$$x = 0 \quad \text{or} \quad x = 4$$
    On solving a simple equation.

   (b)
$$t^2 - 5t = 0$$
$$t(t - 5) = 0$$
    ☞ t is a common factor.
$$t = 0 \quad \text{or} \quad t - 5 = 0$$
$$t = 0 \quad \text{or} \quad t = 5$$

   (c)
$$g^2 + 6g = 0$$
$$g(g + 6) = 0$$
    ☞ Take out the common factor, g.
$$g = 0 \quad \text{or} \quad g + 6 = 0$$
$$g = 0 \quad \text{or} \quad g = -6$$

   (d)
$$z^2 + z = 0$$
$$z(z + 1) = 0$$
    ☞ Don't forget the 1.
$$z = 0 \quad \text{or} \quad z + 1 = 0$$
$$z = 0 \quad \text{or} \quad z = -1$$

   (e)
$$3m^2 - 6m = 0$$
$$3m(m - 2) = 0$$
    ☞ Always take out the largest common factor.
$$3m = 0 \quad \text{or} \quad m - 2 = 0$$
$$m = 0 \quad \text{or} \quad m = 2$$

   (f)
$$7b^2 + 28b = 0$$
$$7b(b + 4) = 0$$
$$7b = 0 \quad \text{or} \quad b + 4 = 0$$
$$b = 0 \quad \text{or} \quad b = -4$$

   (g)
$$4a^2 - 6a = 0$$
$$2a(2a - 3) = 0$$
    ☞ The largest common factor is $2a$.
$$2a = 0 \quad \text{or} \quad 2a - 3 = 0$$
$$a = 0 \quad \text{or} \quad 2a = 3$$
$$a = 0 \quad \text{or} \quad a = 1\tfrac{1}{2}$$

   (h)
$$9h^2 + 3h = 0$$
$$3h(3h + 1) = 0$$
$$3h = 0 \quad \text{or} \quad 3h + 1 = 0$$
$$h = 0 \quad \text{or} \quad 3h = -1$$
$$h = 0 \quad \text{or} \quad h = -\tfrac{1}{3}$$

   (i)
$$8n^2 - 10n = 0$$
$$2n(4n - 5) = 0$$
$$2n = 0 \quad \text{or} \quad 4n - 5 = 0$$
$$n = 0 \quad \text{or} \quad 4n = 5$$
$$n = 0 \quad \text{or} \quad n = 1\tfrac{1}{4}$$

2. Solve, by first factorising a trinomial:

(a) $\qquad x^2 + 9x + 14 = 0$
$\qquad\qquad (\boldsymbol{x + 7)(x + 2) = 0}$ ....☞ What 2 numbers add to 9 and multiply to 14?
$\qquad \boldsymbol{x + 7 = 0 \;\; or \;\; x + 2 = 0}$
$\qquad\quad \boldsymbol{x = -7 \; or \qquad x = -2}$ ....☞ It doesn't matter which number appears first.

(b) $\qquad e^2 - 13e + 40 = 0$
$\qquad\qquad (\boldsymbol{e - 8)(e - 5) = 0}$ ....☞ What 2 numbers add to –13 and multiply to 40?
$\qquad \boldsymbol{e - 8 = 0 \;\; or \;\; e - 5 = 0}$
$\qquad\quad \boldsymbol{e = 8 \;\; or \qquad e = 5}$

(c) $\qquad p^2 - 5p - 24 = 0$
$\qquad\qquad (\boldsymbol{p + 3)(p - 8) = 0}$ ....☞ What 2 numbers add to –5 and multiply to –24?
$\qquad \boldsymbol{p + 3 = 0 \;\; or \;\; p - 8 = 0}$
$\qquad\quad \boldsymbol{p = -3 \;\; or \qquad p = 8}$

(d) $\qquad n^2 - 2n - 35 = 0$ $\qquad$ (e) $\qquad k^2 + 10k + 16 = 0$ $\qquad$ (f) $\qquad d^2 - d - 30 = 0$
$\qquad\quad (\boldsymbol{n + 5)(n - 7) = 0}$ $\qquad\qquad (\boldsymbol{k + 8)(k + 2) = 0}$ $\qquad\qquad (\boldsymbol{d - 6)(d + 5) = 0}$
$\quad \boldsymbol{n + 5 = 0 \;\; or \; n - 7 = 0}$ $\qquad \boldsymbol{k + 8 = 0 \;\;\; or \;\; k + 2 = 0}$ $\qquad \boldsymbol{d - 6 = 0 \;\; or \;\; d + 5 = 0}$
$\qquad \boldsymbol{n = -5 \;\; or \qquad n = 7}$ $\qquad\quad \boldsymbol{k = -8 \; or \qquad k = -2}$ $\qquad\quad \boldsymbol{d = 6 \;\; or \qquad d = -5}$

(g) $\qquad s^2 + 4s - 12 = 0$ $\qquad$ (h) $\qquad u^2 - 9u + 20 = 0$ $\qquad$ (i) $\qquad m^2 + 3m - 18 = 0$
$\qquad\quad (\boldsymbol{s + 6)(s - 2) = 0}$ $\qquad\qquad (\boldsymbol{u - 5)(u - 4) = 0}$ $\qquad\qquad (\boldsymbol{m + 6)(m - 3) = 0}$
$\quad \boldsymbol{s + 6 = 0 \;\; or \; s - 2 = 0}$ $\qquad \boldsymbol{u - 5 = 0 \;\; or \;\; u - 4 = 0}$ $\qquad \boldsymbol{m + 6 = 0 \;\; or \;\; m - 3 = 0}$
$\qquad \boldsymbol{s = -6 \; or \qquad s = 2}$ $\qquad\quad \boldsymbol{u = 5 \;\; or \qquad u = 4}$ $\qquad\quad \boldsymbol{m = -6 \; or \qquad m = 3}$

3. Solve (you might need to use the cross method to factorise):

(a) $\qquad 2x^2 + 7x + 3 = 0$
$\qquad\quad (\boldsymbol{2x + 1)(x + 3) = 0}$
$\boldsymbol{2x + 1 = 0 \;\; or \;\; x + 3 = 0}$
$\qquad \boldsymbol{2x = -1 \;\; or \qquad x = -3}$
$\qquad\quad \boldsymbol{x = -\dfrac{1}{2} \;\; or \qquad x = -3}$

$$2x \times 3 + x \times 1 = \boldsymbol{7x} \checkmark$$

(b) $\qquad 5x^2 - 27x + 10 = 0$
$\qquad\quad (\boldsymbol{5x - 2)(x - 5) = 0}$
$\boldsymbol{5x - 2 = 0 \;\; or \;\; x - 5 = 0}$
$\qquad \boldsymbol{5x = 2 \;\; or \qquad x = 5}$
$\qquad\quad \boldsymbol{x = \dfrac{2}{5} \;\; or \qquad x = 5}$

$$5x \times -5 + x \times -2 = \boldsymbol{-27x} \checkmark$$

(c) $\qquad 3x^2 + 16x - 12 = 0$ $\qquad\qquad$ (d) $\qquad 8x^2 + 6x - 9 = 0$
$\qquad\quad (\boldsymbol{3x - 2)(x + 6) = 0}$ $\qquad\qquad\qquad (\boldsymbol{4x - 3)(2x + 3) = 0}$
$\boldsymbol{3x - 2 = 0 \;\; or \;\; x + 6 = 0}$ $\qquad\qquad \boldsymbol{4x - 3 = 0 \;\; or \;\; 2x + 3 = 0}$
$\qquad \boldsymbol{3x = 2 \;\; or \qquad x = -6}$ $\qquad\qquad\quad \boldsymbol{4x = 3 \;\; or \qquad 2x = -3}$
$\qquad\quad \boldsymbol{x = \dfrac{2}{3} \;\; or \qquad x = -6}$ $\qquad\qquad\qquad \boldsymbol{x = \dfrac{3}{4} \;\; or \qquad x = -1\dfrac{1}{2}}$

FURTHER QUADRATIC EQUATIONS Summary

To solve a quadratic equation using factorisation, the equation must be equal to 0.
That's because we're using the rule: 'If two numbers multiply to zero, one must be zero.'

0 is the only number with this property.
If two numbers multiply to 8, say, it doesn't mean that one must be 8.
The two numbers could be 2 and 4, for example, or 16 and $\frac{1}{2}$.

Example:

Solve: (a) $x^2 = 5x - 6$ (b) $a^2 + 3a = 70$
        (c) $t^2 = t$ (d) $m^2 - 4m - 5 = 7$

Solution:

(a)
$$x^2 = 5x - 6$$
$$x^2 - 5x + 6 = 0$$
$$(x - 3)(x - 2) = 0$$
$$x - 3 = 0 \text{ or } x - 2 = 0$$
$$x = 3 \text{ or } x = 2$$

(b)
$$a^2 + 3a = 70$$
$$a^2 + 3a - 70 = 0$$
$$(a + 10)(a - 7) = 0$$
$$a + 10 = 0 \text{ or } a - 7 = 0$$
$$a = -10 \text{ or } a = 7$$

(c)
$$t^2 = t$$
$$t^2 - t = 0$$
$$t(t - 1) = 0$$
$$t = 0 \text{ or } t - 1 = 0$$
$$t = 0 \text{ or } t = 1$$

(d)
$$m^2 - 4m - 5 = 7$$
$$m^2 - 4m - 12 = 0$$
$$(m - 6)(m + 2) = 0$$
$$m - 6 = 0 \text{ or } m + 2 = 0$$
$$m = 6 \text{ or } m = -2$$

Even if the quadratic equation is factorised we still must set it equal to 0.
We might need to expand first, set the equation equal to 0, and then factorise again.

Example:

(a) $(x + 4)(x + 3) = 2$ (b) $h(h - 5) = 14$
(c) $(q + 3)(q + 5) = 35$ (d) $(e - 6)(e - 4) = 35$

Solution:

(a)
$$(x + 4)(x + 3) = 2$$
$$x^2 + 3x + 4x + 12 = 2$$
$$x^2 + 7x + 10 = 0$$
$$(x + 5)(x + 2) = 0$$
$$x + 5 = 0 \text{ or } x + 2 = 0$$
$$x = -5 \text{ or } x = -2$$

(b)
$$h(h - 5) = 14$$
$$h^2 - 5h = 14$$
$$h^2 - 5h - 14 = 0$$
$$(h - 7)(h + 2) = 0$$
$$h - 7 = 0 \text{ or } h + 2 = 0$$
$$h = 7 \text{ or } h = -2$$

(c)
$$(q + 3)(q + 5) = 35$$
$$q^2 + 5q + 3q + 15 = 35$$
$$q^2 + 8q - 20 = 0$$
$$(q - 2)(q + 10) = 0$$
$$q - 2 = 0 \text{ or } q + 10 = 0$$
$$q = 2 \text{ or } q = -10$$

(d)
$$(e - 6)(e - 4) = 35$$
$$e^2 - 4e - 6e + 24 = 35$$
$$e^2 - 10e - 11 = 0$$
$$(e - 11)(e + 1) = 0$$
$$e - 11 = 0 \text{ or } e + 1 = 0$$
$$e = 11 \text{ or } e = -1$$

1. Solve:

   (a) $y^2 = 7y + 30$

   (b) $e^2 = 10e - 24$

   (c) $p^2 - 9p = 22$

   (d) $w^2 + 11w = 12$

   (e) $b^2 = b$

   (f) $f^2 = 5f$

   (g) $a^2 + 4a - 1 = 20$

   (h) $z^2 - 7z + 10 = 28$

   (i) $x^2 + 8x + 15 = 24$

2. Solve:

   (a) $(x + 2)(x + 5) = 4$

   (b) $(a - 3)(a + 7) = 11$

   (c) $(e - 4)(e - 5) = 56$

   (d) $p(p - 3) = 10$

   (e) $d(d + 1) = 42$

   (f) $(y - 1)(y + 1) = 80$

   (g) $(m + 6)(m - 2) = 33$

   (h) $(n + 8)(n + 8) = 1$

   (i) $(h - 4)(h - 9) = -4$

FURTHER QUADRATIC EQUATIONS Summary

1. Solve:

(a)
$$y^2 = 7y + 30$$
$$y^2 - 7y - 30 = 0$$ ☞ First set the equation equal to zero,
$$(y - 10)(y + 3) = 0$$ then factorise,
$$y - 10 = 0 \quad \text{or} \quad y + 3 = 0$$ and solve two simple equations.
$$y = 10 \quad \text{or} \quad y = -3$$

(b)
$$e^2 = 10e - 24$$
$$e^2 - 10e + 24 = 0$$
$$(e - 6)(e - 4) = 0$$
$$e - 6 = 0 \quad \text{or} \quad e - 4 = 0$$
$$e = 6 \quad \text{or} \quad e = 4$$ ☞ Check, by substitution in the original equation, that you have the right answer.

(c)
$$p^2 - 9p = 22$$
$$p^2 - 9p - 22 = 0$$
$$(p - 11)(p + 2) = 0$$ ☞ What 2 numbers add to –9 and multiply to –22?
$$p - 11 = 0 \quad \text{or} \quad p + 2 = 0$$
$$p = 11 \quad \text{or} \quad p = -2$$

(d)
$$w^2 + 11w = 12$$
$$w^2 + 11w - 12 = 0$$
$$(w + 12)(w - 1) = 0$$
$$w + 12 = 0 \quad \text{or} \quad w - 1 = 0$$
$$w = -12 \quad \text{or} \quad w = 1$$

(e)
$$b^2 = b$$ ☞ Be careful with this type of question.
$$b^2 - b = 0$$ It should be done in the same way: set = 0,
$$b(b - 1) = 0$$ factorise, and solve.
$$b = 0 \quad \text{or} \quad b - 1 = 0$$
$$b = 0 \quad \text{or} \quad b = 1$$

(f)
$$f^2 = 5f$$
$$f^2 - 5f = 0$$
$$f(f - 5) = 0$$ ☞ f is a common factor.
$$f = 0 \quad \text{or} \quad f - 5 = 0$$
$$f = 0 \quad \text{or} \quad f = 5$$

(g)
$$a^2 + 4a - 1 = 20$$
$$a^2 + 4a - 21 = 0$$
$$(a + 7)(a - 3) = 0$$
$$a + 7 = 0 \quad \text{or} \quad a - 3 = 0$$
$$a = -7 \quad \text{or} \quad a = 3$$

(h)
$$z^2 - 7z + 10 = 28$$
$$z^2 - 7z - 18 = 0$$
$$(z - 9)(z + 2) = 0$$
$$z - 9 = 0 \quad \text{or} \quad z + 2 = 0$$
$$z = 9 \quad \text{or} \quad z = -2$$

(i)
$$x^2 + 8x + 15 = 24$$
$$x^2 + 8x - 9 = 0$$
$$(x + 9)(x - 1) = 0$$
$$x + 9 = 0 \quad \text{or} \quad x - 1 = 0$$
$$x = -9 \quad \text{or} \quad x = 1$$

2. Solve:

(a) $(x + 2)(x + 5) = 4$
$x^2 + 5x + 2x + 10 = 4$ ☞ First expand.
$x^2 + 7x + 10 = 4$
$x^2 + 7x + 6 = 0$ ☞ Subtract 4 from both sides of the equation.
$(x + 6)(x + 1) = 0$ Factorise.
$x + 6 = 0$ or $x + 1 = 0$
$x = -6$ or $x = -1$

(b) $(a - 3)(a + 7) = 11$
$a^2 + 7a - 3a - 21 = 11$ ☞ Expand.
$a^2 + 4a - 21 = 11$
$a^2 + 4a - 32 = 0$ ☞ Subtract 11 from both sides,
$(a + 8)(a - 4) = 0$ and factorise.
$a + 8 = 0$ or $a - 4 = 0$
$a = -8$ or $a = 4$

(c) $(e - 4)(e - 5) = 56$
$e^2 - 5e - 4e + 20 = 56$ ☞ Expanding the binomial product.
$e^2 - 9e + 20 = 56$
$e^2 - 9e - 36 = 0$ ☞ Subtracting 56 from both sides of the equation.
$(e - 12)(e + 3) = 0$
$e - 12 = 0$ or $e + 3 = 0$
$e = 12$ or $e = -3$ ☞ Check your answer by substituting.

(d) $p(p - 3) = 10$
$p^2 - 3p = 10$
$p^2 - 3p - 10 = 0$
$(p - 5)(p + 2) = 0$
$p - 5 = 0$ or $p + 2 = 0$
$p = 5$ or $p = -2$

(e) $d(d + 1) = 42$
$d^2 + d = 42$
$d^2 + d - 42 = 0$
$(d + 7)(d - 6) = 0$
$d + 7 = 0$ or $d - 6 = 0$
$d = -7$ or $d = 6$

(f) $(y - 1)(y + 1) = 80$
$y^2 - 1 = 80$ ☞ Expanding a sum by difference.
$y^2 - 81 = 0$ ☞ We now have another difference of two squares.
$(y + 9)(y - 9) = 0$
$y + 9 = 0$ or $y - 9 = 0$
$y = -9$ or $y = 9$

(g) $(m + 6)(m - 2) = 33$
$m^2 - 2m + 6m - 12 = 33$
$m^2 + 4m - 12 = 33$
$m^2 + 4m - 45 = 0$
$(m + 9)(m - 5) = 0$
$m + 9 = 0$ or $m - 5 = 0$
$m = -9$ or $m = 5$

(h) $(n + 8)(n + 8) = 1$
$n^2 + 8n + 8n + 64 = 1$
$n^2 + 16n + 64 = 1$
$n^2 + 16n + 63 = 0$
$(n + 9)(n + 7) = 0$
$n + 9 = 0$ or $n + 7 = 0$
$n = -9$ or $n = -7$

(i) $(h - 4)(h - 9) = -4$
$h^2 - 9h - 4h + 36 = -4$
$h^2 - 13h + 36 = -4$
$h^2 - 13h + 40 = 0$
$(h - 8)(h - 5) = 0$
$h - 8 = 0$ or $h - 5 = 0$
$h = 8$ or $h = 5$

SOLVING EQUATIONS WITH SQUARES Summary

> If $x^2 = 9$, there are two solutions, $x = 3$ or $x = -3$.
> The symbol $\pm$ means 'plus or minus'. $x = \pm 4$ means $x = 4$ or $x = -4$.

Example:
Solve: **(a)** $x^2 = 25$ **(b)** $a^2 = 121$ **(c)** $n^2 = 400$ **(d)** $3k^2 = 300$

Solution:

(a) $x^2 = 25$
$\quad x = 5$ or $x = -5$

(b) $a^2 = 121$
$\quad a = 11$ or $a = -11$

(c) $n^2 = 400$
$\quad n = \pm 20$

(d) $3k^2 = 300$
$\quad k^2 = 100$
$\quad k = \pm 10$

> To solve an equation like $x^2 - 36 = 0$, we can use either of two methods:
> factorising (difference of two squares) or taking square roots.
>
> $\qquad x^2 - 36 = 0 \qquad\qquad$ or $\qquad x^2 - 36 = 0$
> $\qquad (x + 6)(x - 6) = 0 \qquad\qquad\qquad x^2 = 36$
> $x + 6 = 0$ or $x - 6 = 0 \qquad\qquad\quad x = \pm 6$
> $\qquad x = -6 \quad$ or $\quad x = 6$
>
> We might need to take the square root of both sides of an equation
> and then solve two simple equations.

Example:
Solve: **(a)** $(x + 6)^2 = 16$ **(b)** $(y - 8)^2 = 81$ **(c)** $(5 - p)^2 = 9$

Solution:

(a) $\qquad (x + 6)^2 = 16$
$x + 6 = 4$ or $x + 6 = -4$
$\quad x = -2 \quad$ or $\quad x = -10$

(b) $\qquad (y - 8)^2 = 81$
$y - 8 = 9$ or $y - 8 = -9$
$\quad y = 17 \quad$ or $\quad y = -1$

(c) $\qquad (5 - p)^2 = 9$
$5 - p = 3$ or $5 - p = -3$
$\quad p = 2 \quad$ or $\quad p = 8$

> The solution to an equation might involve a surd. A surd is a square root of a number that is
> not a perfect square. $\sqrt{2}$ is a surd. $\sqrt{4}$ is not a surd because $\sqrt{4} = 2$.
> Ordinary numbers and surds are not like terms, so cannot be simplified.
> We usually write the numbers first, so we don't confuse, say, $\sqrt{7} - 2$ with $\sqrt{7 - 2}$.

Example:
Solve: **(a)** $(x + 2)^2 = 7$ **(b)** $(z - 7)^2 = 5$

Solution:

(a) $\qquad (x + 2)^2 = 7$
$x + 2 = \sqrt{7}$ or $x + 2 = -\sqrt{7}$
$x = -2 + \sqrt{7}$ or $x = -2 - \sqrt{7}$

(b) $\qquad (z - 7)^2 = 5$
$z - 7 = \sqrt{5}$ or $z - 7 = -\sqrt{5}$
$z = 7 + \sqrt{5}$ or $z = 7 - \sqrt{5}$

> We could write the answer in one expression.
> Instead of saying $-2 + \sqrt{7}$ or $-2 - \sqrt{7}$ we could say $-2 \pm \sqrt{7}$.

Example:
Solve: **(a)** $(t - 3)^2 = 2$ **(b)** $(k + 5)^2 = 11$

Solution:

(a) $(t - 3)^2 = 2$
$\quad t - 3 = \pm \sqrt{2}$
$\qquad t = 3 \pm \sqrt{2}$

(b) $(k + 5)^2 = 11$
$\quad k + 5 = \pm \sqrt{11}$
$\qquad k = -5 \pm \sqrt{11}$

1. Solve:

   (a) $x^2 = 64$

   (b) $t^2 = 144$

   (c) $z^2 = 49$

   (d) $c^2 = 1$

   (e) $5a^2 = 20$

   (f) $7n^2 = 63$

2. Solve, by factorising:

   (a) $m^2 - 100 = 0$

   (b) $k^2 - 81 = 0$

   (c) $n^2 - 1 = 0$

3. Solve, by taking square roots:

   (a) $b^2 - 4 = 0$

   (b) $g^2 - 9 = 0$

   (c) $d^2 - 16 = 0$

4. Solve:

   (a) $(x + 5)^2 = 36$

   (b) $(a - 4)^2 = 121$

   (c) $(t - 3)^2 = 1$

   (d) $(h + 1)^2 = 25$

   (e) $(7 - e)^2 = 4$

   (f) $(k + 10)^2 = 100$

5. Solve, giving the answer as two different expressions:

   (a) $(t - 2)^2 = 5$

   (b) $(x + 6)^2 = 6$

   (c) $(a - 9)^2 = 2$

   (d) $(k - 5)^2 = 3$

   (e) $(y + 1)^2 = 7$

   (f) $(g + 4)^2 = 11$

6. Solve, giving the answer in one expression:

   (a) $(p - 3)^2 = 17$

   (b) $(h + 8)^2 = 13$

   (c) $(b - 7)^2 = 3$

   (d) $(c + 2)^2 = 6$

   (e) $(q - 1)^2 = 2$

   (f) $(r - 10)^2 = 10$

1. Solve:

   (a) $x^2 = 64$
      $x = 8$ or $x = -8$ .... ☞ There must be two solutions.

   (b) $t^2 = 144$
      $t = 12$ or $t = -12$

   (c) $z^2 = 49$
      $z = 7$ or $z = -7$

   (d) $c^2 = 1$
      $c = 1$ or $c = -1$ .... ☞ Don't forget the negative solution.

   (e) $5a^2 = 20$
      $a^2 = 4$ .... ☞ First divide both sides of the equation by 5;
      $a = 2$ or $a = -2$ then take square roots.

   (f) $7n^2 = 63$
      $n^2 = 9$
      $n = 3$ or $n = -3$

2. Solve, by factorising:

   (a) $m^2 - 100 = 0$
      $(m + 10)(m - 10) = 0$ .... ☞ Difference of two squares: $m^2 - 100 = m^2 - 10^2$
   $m + 10 = 0$ or $m - 10 = 0$
      $m = -10$ or $m = 10$

   (b) $k^2 - 81 = 0$
      $(k + 9)(k - 9) = 0$ .... ☞ $k^2 - 81 = k^2 - 9^2$
    $k + 9 = 0$ or $k - 9 = 0$
      $k = -9$ or $k = 9$

   (c) $n^2 - 1 = 0$
      $(n + 1)(n - 1) = 0$ .... ☞ $n^2 - 1 = n^2 - 1^2$
    $n + 1 = 0$ or $n - 1 = 0$
        $n = -1$ or $n = 1$

3. Solve, by taking square roots:

   (a) $b^2 - 4 = 0$
      $b^2 = 4$ .... ☞ Add 4 to both sides of the equation.
   $b = 2$ or $b = -2$ Then take square roots.

   (b) $g^2 - 9 = 0$
      $g^2 = 9$
   $g = 3$ or $g = -3$

   (c) $d^2 - 16 = 0$
            $d^2 = 16$
   $d = 4$ or $d = -4$

4. Solve:

(a) $(x + 5)^2 = 36$

$x + 5 = 6$ or $x + 5 = -6$ .... ☞ Taking square roots.

$x = 1$ or $x = -11$ Subtracting 5 from both sides of both equations.

(b) $(a - 4)^2 = 121$

$a - 4 = 11$ or $a - 4 = -11$ .... ☞ Taking square roots.

$a = 15$ or $a = -7$ Adding 4 to both sides of both equations.

(c) $(t - 3)^2 = 1$

$t - 3 = 1$ or $t - 3 = -1$

$t = 4$ or $t = 2$ .... ☞ Check by substitution in the original equation.

(d) $(h + 1)^2 = 25$ (e) $(7 - e)^2 = 4$ (f) $(k + 10)^2 = 100$

    $h + 1 = 5$ or $h + 1 = -5$ $7 - e = 2$ or $7 - e = -2$ $k + 10 = 10$ or $k + 10 = -10$

    $h = 4$ or $h = -6$ $e = 5$ or $e = 9$ $k = 0$ or $k = -20$

5. Solve, giving the answer as two different expressions:

(a) $(t - 2)^2 = 5$ .... ☞ 5 is not a perfect square

    $t - 2 = \sqrt{5}$ or $t - 2 = -\sqrt{5}$ so the answer involves a surd.

    $t = 2 + \sqrt{5}$ or $t = 2 - \sqrt{5}$ $\sqrt{5} + 2$ or $- \sqrt{5} + 2$ is the same thing, but we

                               usually write the numbers first.

(b) $(x + 6)^2 = 6$ (c) $(a - 9)^2 = 2$

    $x + 6 = \sqrt{6}$ or $x + 6 = -\sqrt{6}$ $a - 9 = \sqrt{2}$ or $a - 9 = -\sqrt{2}$

    $x = -6 + \sqrt{6}$ or $x = -6 - \sqrt{6}$ $a = 9 + \sqrt{2}$ or $a = 9 - \sqrt{2}$

(d) $(k - 5)^2 = 3$ (e) $(y + 1)^2 = 7$ (f) $(g + 4)^2 = 11$

   $k - 5 = \sqrt{3}$ or $k - 5 = -\sqrt{3}$ $y + 1 = \sqrt{7}$ or $y + 1 = -\sqrt{7}$ $g + 4 = \sqrt{11}$ or $g + 4 = -\sqrt{11}$

   $k = 5 + \sqrt{3}$ or $k = 5 - \sqrt{3}$ $y = -1 + \sqrt{7}$ or $y = -1 - \sqrt{7}$ $g = -4 + \sqrt{11}$ or $g = -4 - \sqrt{11}$

6. Solve, giving the answer in one expression:

(a) $(p - 3)^2 = 17$

    $p - 3 = \pm\sqrt{17}$ .... ☞ This is the same as $p - 3 = \sqrt{17}$ or $p - 3 = -\sqrt{17}$.

    $p = 3 \pm \sqrt{17}$ .... ☞ Adding 3 to both sides of the equation.

(b) $(h + 8)^2 = 13$ (c) $(b - 7)^2 = 3$

    $h + 8 = \pm\sqrt{13}$ $b - 7 = \pm \sqrt{3}$

    $h = -8 \pm \sqrt{13}$ $b = 7 \pm \sqrt{3}$

(d) $(c + 2)^2 = 6$ (e) $(q - 1)^2 = 2$ (f) $(r - 10)^2 = 10$

    $c + 2 = \pm \sqrt{6}$ $q - 1 = \pm \sqrt{2}$ $r - 10 = \pm \sqrt{10}$

    $c = -2 \pm \sqrt{6}$ $q = 1 \pm \sqrt{2}$ $r = 10 \pm \sqrt{10}$

> We know that $(x + y)^2 = x^2 + 2xy + y^2$ and $(x - y)^2 = x^2 - 2xy + y^2$.
> To determine whether a trinomial is a perfect square we need to decide whether it
> can be expressed as either $x^2 + 2xy + y^2$ or $x^2 - 2xy + y^2$.

Example:
Determine whether these are perfect squares:
(a) $x^2 + 18x + 81$ **(b)** $m^2 - 6m + 36$ **(c)** $16a^2 + 56a + 49$ **(d)** $25y^2 - 20yz + 4z^2$

Solution:
(a) $x^2 + 18x + 81 = x^2 + 2 \times x \times 9 + 9^2$
                    $= (x + 9)^2$

(b) $m^2 - 6m + 36 = m^2 - 2 \times m \times 3 + 6^2$
        Not a perfect square.

(c) $16a^2 + 56a + 49 = (4a)^2 + 2 \times 4a \times 7 + 7^2$
                    $= (4a + 7)^2$

(d) $25y^2 - 20yz + 4z^2 = (5y)^2 - 2 \times 5y \times 2z + (2z)^2$
                    $= (5y - 2z)^2$

> To complete the square simply means to make into a perfect square.

Example:
What must be added to each expression to complete the square?
(a) $h^2 - 6h$ **(b)** $k^2 + 24k$ **(c)** $64e^2 - 16e$ **(d)** $9p^2 + 30pq$

Solution:
(a) $h^2 - 6h = h^2 - 2 \times h \times 3$
   We need to add $3^2 = 9$.

(b) $k^2 + 24k = k^2 + 2 \times k \times 12$
   We need to add $12^2 = 144$.

(c) $64e^2 - 16e = (8e)^2 - 2 \times 8e \times 1$
   We need to add $1^2 = 1$.

(d) $9p^2 + 30pq = (3p)^2 + 2 \times 3p \times 5q$
   We need to add $(5q)^2 = 25q^2$.

> We can add a number or a term in order to complete a square.

Example:
Add a term to each expression to complete the square, and then express it as a square:
(a) $x^2 + 10x$ **(b)** $a^2 - 14a$ **(c)** $q^2 + 9q$ **(d)** $121 - 22d$ **(e)** $9n^2 - 42n$ **(f)** $64a^2 + 48ab$

Solution:
(a) $x^2 + 10x = x^2 + 2 \times x \times 5$
$x^2 + 10x + 5^2 = x^2 + 10x + 25$
           $= (x + 5)^2$

(b) $a^2 - 14a = a^2 - 2 \times a \times 7$
$a^2 - 14a + 7^2 = a^2 - 14a + 49$
           $= (a - 7)^2$

(c) $q^2 + 9q = q^2 + 2 \times q \times 4.5$
$q^2 + 9q + (4.5)^2 = q^2 + 9q + 20.25$
           $= (q + 4.5)^2$

(d) $121 - 22d = 11^2 - 2 \times 11 \times d$
$121 - 22d + d^2 = (11 - d)^2$

(e) $9n^2 - 42n = (3n)^2 - 2 \times 3n \times 7$
$(3n)^2 - 42n + 7^2 = 9n^2 - 42n + 49$
           $= (3n - 7)^2$

(f) $64a^2 + 48ab = (8a)^2 + 2 \times 8a \times 3b$
$(8a)^2 + 48ab + (3b)^2 = 64a^2 + 48ab + 9b^2$
           $= (8a + 3b)^2$

1. Determine whether the following are perfect squares, and if so, express them as a square:

   (a) $x^2 + 12x + 36$

   (b) $a^2 - 14a + 49$

   (c) $e^2 + 4e + 4$

   (d) $p^2 - 16p - 64$

   (e) $n^2 + 11n + 121$

   (f) $u^2 - 2u + 1$

   (g) $9y^2 - 12y + 16$

   (h) $m^2 + 2mn + n^2$

   (i) $4a^2 + 44a + 121$

2. What must be added to each expression to complete the square?

   (a) $p^2 + 18p$

   (b) $u^2 - 10u$

   (c) $k^2 - 40k$

   (d) $d^2 + 22d$

   (e) $x^2 + 2x$

   (f) $m^2 - 26m$

   (g) $n^2 - 5n$

   (h) $4t^2 + 36t$

   (i) $25e^2 + 60e$

   (j) $100p^2 - 60p$

   (k) $9a^2 + 6ab$

   (l) $16c^2 - 56cd$

3. Add a term to each expression to complete the square, and then express it as a square:

   (a) $a^2 + 6a$ = _____

   (b) $h^2 - 10h$ = _____

   (c) $z^2 - 24z$ = _____

   (d) $n^2 + 20n$ = _____

   (e) $q^2 - 4q$ = _____

   (f) $w^2 + 2w$ = _____

   (g) $e^2 - e$ = _____

   (h) $16s^2 + 72s$ = _____

   (i) $49d^2 - 42de$ = _____

1. Determine whether the following are perfect squares,
    and if so, express them as a square:

    (a) $x^2 + 12x + 36 = x^2 + 2 \times x \times 6 + 6^2$ .... ☞ It is of the form $x^2 + 2xy + y^2$ so it is
         $\qquad\qquad\qquad = (x + 6)^2$ a perfect square.

    (b) $a^2 - 14a + 49 = a^2 - 2 \times a \times 7 + 7^2$ .... ☞ It is of the form $x^2 - 2xy + y^2$ so it is a perfect square.
         $\qquad\qquad\qquad = (a - 7)^2$

    (c) $e^2 + 4e + 4 = e^2 + 2 \times e \times 2 + 2^2$ .... ☞ Of the form $x^2 + 2xy + y^2$.
         $\qquad\qquad\qquad = (e + 2)^2$

    (d) $p^2 - 16p - 64 = p^2 - 2 \times p \times 8 - 8^2$ .... ☞ The last term of a perfect square is always added.
                    Not a perfect square.   The operation signs are wrong.

    (e) $n^2 + 11n + 121 = n^2 + 2 \times n \times 5.5 + 11^2$ .... ☞ It is not of the form $x^2 + 2xy + y^2$.
                    Not a perfect square.

    (f) $u^2 - 2u + 1 = u^2 - 2 \times u \times 1 + 1^2$
         $\qquad\qquad\quad = (u - 1)^2$

    (g) $9y^2 - 12y + 16 = (3y)^2 - 2 \times 3y \times 2 + 4^2$ .... ☞ Not of the form $x^2 + 2xy + y^2$.
                    Not a perfect square.

    (h) $m^2 + 2mn + n^2 = m^2 + 2 \times m \times n + n^2$
         $\qquad\qquad\qquad\;\; = (m + n)^2$

    (i) $4a^2 + 44a + 121 = (2a)^2 + 2 \times 2a \times 11 + 11^2$
         $\qquad\qquad\qquad\;\;\; = (2a + 11)^2$

2. What must be added to each expression to complete the square?

    (a) $p^2 + 18p = p^2 + 2 \times p \times 9$ .... ☞ A perfect square is of the form $x^2 + 2xy + y^2$.
         We need to add $9^2 = $ **81.**

    (b) $u^2 - 10u = u^2 - 2 \times u \times 5$ .... ☞ $10u = 2 \times u \times 5$
         We need to add $5^2 = $ **25.**

    (c) $k^2 - 40k = k^2 - 2 \times k \times 20$ .... ☞ Ask yourself: $40k = 2 \times k \times ?$
         We need to add $20^2 = $ **400.**

    (d) $d^2 + 22d = d^2 + 2 \times d \times 11$ (e) $x^2 + 2x = x^2 + 2 \times x \times 1$ (f) $m^2 - 26m = m^2 - 2 \times m \times 13$
         We need to add $11^2 = $ **121.**   We need to add $1^2 = $ **1.**   We need to add $13^2 = $ **169.**

    (g) $n^2 - 5n = n^2 - 2 \times n \times 2.5$ .... ☞ $n^2 - 2 \times n \times 2\frac{1}{2}$ is the same thing.
         We need to add $2.5^2 = $ **6.25.**   or $(2\frac{1}{2})^2 = 6\frac{1}{4}$

(h) $4t^2 + 36t = (2t)^2 + 2 \times 2t \times 9$ ☞ A perfect square is of the form $x^2 + 2xy + y^2$.
We need to add $9^2 = \mathbf{81}$.

(i) $25e^2 + 60e = (5e)^2 + 2 \times 5e \times 6$ ☞ $25e^2 = (5e)^2$; $60e = 2 \times 5e \times ?$
We need to add $6^2 = \mathbf{36}$.

(j) $100p^2 - 60p = (10p)^2 - 2 \times 10p \times 3$ ☞ It needs to be of the form $x^2 - 2xy + y^2$.
We need to add $3^2 = \mathbf{9}$.

(k) $9a^2 + 6ab = (3a)^2 + 2 \times 3a \times b$
We need to add $\mathbf{b^2}$.

(l) $16c^2 - 56cd = (4c)^2 - 2 \times 4c \times 7d$ ☞ Ask yourself: $56cd = 2 \times 4c \times ?$
We need to add $(7d)^2 = \mathbf{49d^2}$.

3. Add a term to each of the following expressions to complete the square, and then express it as a square:

(a) $a^2 + 6a = \mathbf{a^2 + 2 \times a \times 3}$ ☞ A perfect square is of the form $x^2 + 2xy + y^2$.
$a^2 + 6a + 3^2 = \mathbf{a^2 + 6a + 9}$
$\qquad = \mathbf{(a + 3)^2}$

(b) $h^2 - 10h = \mathbf{h^2 - 2 \times h \times 5}$ ☞ A perfect square is of the form $x^2 - 2xy + y^2$.
$h^2 - 10h + 5^2 = \mathbf{h^2 - 10h + 25}$
$\qquad = \mathbf{(h - 5)^2}$

(c) $z^2 - 24z = \mathbf{z^2 - 2 \times z \times 12}$
$z^2 - 24z + 12^2 = \mathbf{z^2 - 24z + 144}$
$\qquad = \mathbf{(z - 12)^2}$

(d) $n^2 + 20n = \mathbf{n^2 + 2 \times n \times 10}$
$n^2 + 20n + 10^2 = \mathbf{n^2 + 20n + 100}$
$\qquad = \mathbf{(n + 10)^2}$

(e) $q^2 - 4q = \mathbf{q^2 - 2 \times q \times 2}$
$q^2 - 4q + 2^2 = \mathbf{q^2 - 4q + 4}$
$\qquad = \mathbf{(q - 2)^2}$

(f) $w^2 + 2w = \mathbf{w^2 + 2 \times w \times 1}$
$w^2 + 2w + 1^2 = \mathbf{w^2 + 2w + 1}$
$\qquad = \mathbf{(w + 1)^2}$

(g) $e^2 - e = \mathbf{e^2 - 2 \times e \times \frac{1}{2}}$
$e^2 - e + (\frac{1}{2})^2 = \mathbf{e^2 - e + \frac{1}{4}}$
$\qquad = \mathbf{(e - \frac{1}{2})^2}$ ☞ or $e^2 - e + 0.25 = (e - 0.5)^2$

(h) $16s^2 + 72s = \mathbf{(4s)^2 + 2 \times 4s \times 9}$
$(4s)^2 + 72s + 9^2 = \mathbf{16s^2 + 72s + 81}$
$\qquad = \mathbf{(4s + 9)^2}$

(i) $49d^2 - 42de = \mathbf{(7d)^2 - 2 \times 7d \times 3e}$
$(7d)^2 - 42de + (3e)^2 = \mathbf{49d^2 - 42de + 9e^2}$
$\qquad = \mathbf{(7d - 3e)^2}$

Quadratic equations can be solved by first completing the square.

Example:

Solve, by completing the square:

(a) $x^2 + 8x = 9$　　(b) $m^2 + 10m = 144$　　(c) $a^2 - 6a = 40$　　(d) $4x^2 + 12x = 27$

Solution:

(a)
$$x^2 + 8x = 9$$
$$x^2 + 8x + 16 = 9 + 16$$
$$(x + 4)^2 = 25$$
$$x + 4 = 5 \quad\text{or}\quad x + 4 = -5$$
$$x = 1 \quad\text{or}\quad x = -9$$

What number must we add to $x^2 + 8x$ to complete the square?
Add 16 to both sides.
The left-hand side is now a perfect square.
Taking square roots.

(b)
$$m^2 + 10m = 144$$
$$m^2 + 10m + 25 = 144 + 25$$
$$(m + 5)^2 = 169$$
$$m + 5 = 13 \quad\text{or}\quad m + 5 = -13$$
$$m = 8 \quad\text{or}\quad m = -18$$

(c)
$$a^2 - 6a = 40$$
$$a^2 - 6a + 9 = 40 + 9$$
$$(a - 3)^2 = 49$$
$$a - 3 = 7 \quad\text{or}\quad a - 3 = -7$$
$$a = 10 \quad\text{or}\quad a = -4$$

(d)
$$4x^2 + 12x = 27$$
$$4x^2 + 12x + 9 = 27 + 9$$
$$(2x + 3)^2 = 36$$
$$2x + 3 = 6 \quad\text{or}\quad 2x + 3 = -6$$
$$2x = 3 \quad\text{or}\quad 2x = -9$$
$$x = 1\tfrac{1}{2} \quad\text{or}\quad x = -4\tfrac{1}{2}$$

We might need to use surds in our answer.

Example:

Solve: (a) $x^2 - 12x = -13$　　(b) $p^2 + 4p = 15$　　(c) $9x^2 - 6x = 29$

Solution:

(a)
$$x^2 - 12x = -13$$
$$x^2 - 12x + 36 = -13 + 36$$
$$(x - 6)^2 = 23$$
$$x - 6 = \pm\sqrt{23}$$
$$x = 6 \pm \sqrt{23}$$

(b)
$$p^2 + 4p = 15$$
$$p^2 + 4p + 4 = 15 + 4$$
$$(p + 2)^2 = 19$$
$$p + 2 = \pm\sqrt{19}$$
$$p = -2 \pm \sqrt{19}$$

(c)
$$9x^2 - 6x = 29$$
$$9x^2 - 6x + 1 = 29 + 1$$
$$(3x - 1)^2 = 30$$
$$3x - 1 = \pm\sqrt{30}$$
$$3x = 1 \pm \sqrt{30}$$
$$x = \frac{1 \pm \sqrt{30}}{3}$$

The method of completing the square can be used instead of factorising a trinomial or when a trinomial cannot be factorised.

Example:

Solve: (a) $x^2 + 14x - 51 = 0$　　(b) $x^2 - 8x + 5 = 0$　　(c) $25x^2 + 20x + 2 = 0$

Solution:

(a)
$$x^2 + 14x - 51 = 0$$
$$x^2 + 14x = 51$$
$$x^2 + 14x + 49 = 51 + 49$$
$$(x + 7)^2 = 100$$
$$x + 7 = 10 \quad\text{or}\quad x + 7 = -10$$
$$x = 3 \quad\text{or}\quad x = -17$$

(b)
$$x^2 - 8x + 5 = 0$$
$$x^2 - 8x = -5$$
$$x^2 - 8x + 16 = -5 + 16$$
$$(x - 4)^2 = 11$$
$$x - 4 = \pm\sqrt{11}$$
$$x = 4 \pm \sqrt{11}$$

(c)
$$25x^2 + 20x + 2 = 0$$
$$25x^2 + 20x + 4 = -2 + 4$$
$$(5x + 2)^2 = 2$$
$$5x + 2 = \pm\sqrt{2}$$
$$5x = -2 \pm \sqrt{2}$$
$$x = \frac{-2 \pm \sqrt{2}}{5}$$

The square root of a negative number is not a real number. We can only solve this type of question when the expression that is squared is equal to a number that is not negative.

1. Solve, by completing the square:

(a) $x^2 + 12x = 64$

(b) $e^2 + 6e = 16$

(c) $p^2 - 16p = 225$

(d) $a^2 - 4a = 45$

(e) $g^2 + 14g = 15$

(f) $u^2 - 18u = -45$

(g) $4x^2 + 20x = 75$

(h) $9d^2 - 24d = 20$

(i) $25k^2 + 60k = -27$

2. Solve:

(a) $a^2 + 2a = 5$

(b) $n^2 - 10n = -18$

(c) $t^2 - 8t = -3$

(d) $16k^2 + 24k = 1$

(e) $144h^2 - 24h = 13$

(f) $49m^2 + 70m = -12$

3. Solve, by completing the square:

(a) $x^2 - 20x + 84 = 0$

(b) $e^2 + 8e + 11 = 0$

(c) $36m^2 - 84m + 46 = 0$

1. Solve, by completing the square:

(a) $\qquad x^2 + 12x = 64$ .... ☞ $x^2 + 12x = x^2 + 2 \times x \times 6$

$x^2 + 12x + 36 = 64 + 36$ We need to add 6^2 to both sides of the equation.

$(x + 6)^2 = 100$

$x + 6 = 10 \quad \text{or} \quad x + 6 = -10$

$x = 4 \qquad \text{or} \qquad x = -16$

(b) $\qquad e^2 + 6e = 16$ .... ☞ $e^2 + 6e = e^2 + 2 \times e \times 3$

$e^2 + 6e + 9 = 16 + 9$ We need to add 3^2.

$(e + 3)^2 = 25$

$e + 3 = 5 \quad \text{or} \quad e + 3 = -5$

$e = 2 \quad \text{or} \qquad e = -8$

(c) $\qquad p^2 - 16p = 225$ .... ☞ What must be added to complete the square?

$p^2 - 16p + 64 = 225 + 64$

$(p - 8)^2 = 289$

$p - 8 = 17 \quad \text{or} \quad p - 8 = -17$

$p = 25 \qquad \text{or} \qquad p = -9$

(d) $\qquad a^2 - 4a = 45$ (e) $\quad g^2 + 14g = 15$ (f) $\qquad u^2 - 18u = -45$

$a^2 - 4a + 4 = 45 + 4$ $g^2 + 14g + 49 = 15 + 49$ $u^2 - 18u + 81 = -45 + 81$

$(a - 2)^2 = 49$ $(g + 7)^2 = 64$ $(u - 9)^2 = 36$

$a - 2 = 7 \quad \text{or} \quad a - 2 = -7$ $g + 7 = 8 \quad \text{or} \quad g + 7 = -8$ $u - 9 = 6 \quad \text{or} \quad u - 9 = -6$

$a = 9 \quad \text{or} \qquad a = -5$ $g = 1 \quad \text{or} \quad g = -15$ $u = 15 \quad \text{or} \quad u = 3$

(g) $\qquad 4x^2 + 20x = 75$ .... ☞ $4x^2 + 20x = (2x)^2 + 2 \times 2x \times 5$

$4x^2 + 20x + 25 = 75 + 25$ We need to add 5^2.

$(2x + 5)^2 = 100$

$2x + 5 = 10 \quad \text{or} \quad 2x + 5 = -10$

$2x = 5 \quad \text{or} \qquad 2x = -15$

$x = 2.5 \text{ or} \qquad x = -7.5$ .... ☞ OR: $\quad x = 2\frac{1}{2} \quad \text{or} \quad x = -7\frac{1}{2}$

(h) $\qquad 9d^2 - 24d = 20$ .... ☞ $9d^2 - 24d = (3d)^2 - 2 \times 3d \times 4$

$9d^2 - 24d + 16 = 20 + 16$ We need to add 4^2 to both sides of the equation.

$(3d - 4)^2 = 36$

$3d - 4 = 6 \quad \text{or} \quad 3d - 4 = -6$

$3d = 10 \quad \text{or} \quad 3d = -2$

$d = 3\frac{1}{3} \quad \text{or} \qquad d = -\frac{2}{3}$

(i) $\qquad 25k^2 + 60k = -27$ .... ☞ $25k^2 + 60k = (5k)^2 + 2 \times 5k \times 6$

$25k^2 + 60k + 36 = -27 + 36$ We need to add 6^2.

$(5k + 6)^2 = 9$

$5k + 6 = 3 \quad \text{or} \quad 5k + 6 = -3$

$5k = -3 \quad \text{or} \quad 5k = -9$

$k = -\frac{3}{5} \quad \text{or} \qquad k = -1\frac{4}{5}$ .... ☞ The answers could be given as decimals.

2. Solve:

(a) $a^2 + 2a = 5$ .... 👉 $a^2 + 2a = a^2 + 2 \times a \times 1$

  $a^2 + 2a + 1 = 5 + 1$ .... 👉 We need to add 1^2 to both sides of the equation.

   $(a + 1)^2 = 6$

  $a + 1 = \sqrt{6}$ or $a + 1 = -\sqrt{6}$

    $a = -1 + \sqrt{6}$ or $a = -1 - \sqrt{6}$ .... 👉 or $a = -1 \pm \sqrt{6}$

(b) $n^2 - 10n = -18$

  $n^2 - 10n + 25 = -18 + 25$

   $(n - 5)^2 = 7$

  $n - 5 = \sqrt{7}$ or $n - 5 = -\sqrt{7}$

    $n = 5 + \sqrt{7}$ or $n = 5 - \sqrt{7}$

(c) $t^2 - 8t = -3$

  $t^2 - 8t + 16 = -3 + 16$

   $(t - 4)^2 = 13$

  $t - 4 = \sqrt{13}$ or $t - 4 = -\sqrt{13}$

    $t = 4 + \sqrt{13}$ or $t = 4 - \sqrt{13}$

(d) $16k^2 + 24k = 1$ .... 👉 $16k^2 + 24k = (4k)^2 + 2 \times 4k \times 3$

  $(4k)^2 + 24k + 9 = 1 + 9$ .... 👉 We need to add 3^2.

   $(4k + 3)^2 = 10$

  $4k + 3 = \sqrt{10}$ or $4k + 3 = -\sqrt{10}$

    $4k = -3 + \sqrt{10}$ or $4k = -3 - \sqrt{10}$

     $k = \dfrac{-3 + \sqrt{10}}{4}$ or $k = \dfrac{-3 - \sqrt{10}}{4}$

(e) $144h^2 - 24h = 13$

  $(12h)^2 - 24h + 1 = 13 + 1$

   $(12h - 1)^2 = 14$

  $12h - 1 = \sqrt{14}$ or $12h - 1 = -\sqrt{14}$

    $12h = 1 + \sqrt{14}$ or $12h = 1 - \sqrt{14}$

     $h = \dfrac{1 + \sqrt{14}}{12}$ or $h = \dfrac{1 - \sqrt{14}}{12}$

(f) $49m^2 + 70m = -12$

  $(7m)^2 + 70m + 25 = -12 + 25$

   $(7m + 5)^2 = 13$

  $7m + 5 = \sqrt{13}$ or $7m + 5 = -\sqrt{13}$

    $7m = -5 + \sqrt{13}$ or $7m = -5 - \sqrt{13}$

     $m = \dfrac{-5 + \sqrt{13}}{7}$ or $m = \dfrac{-5 - \sqrt{13}}{7}$

3. Solve, by completing the square:

(a) $x^2 - 20x + 84 = 0$

   $x^2 - 20x = -84$ .... 👉 $x^2 - 20x = x^2 - 2 \times x \times 10$

  $x^2 - 20x + 100 = -84 + 100$

    $(x - 10)^2 = 16$

  $x - 10 = 4$ or $x - 10 = -4$ .... 👉 We would get the same result if we solved by

     $x = 14$ or $x = 6$ factorising. $x^2 - 20x + 84 = (x - 14)(x - 6)$

(b) $e^2 + 8e + 11 = 0$

    $e^2 + 8e = -11$

  $e^2 + 8e + 16 = -11 + 16$

    $(e + 4)^2 = 5$

  $e + 4 = \sqrt{5}$ or $e + 4 = -\sqrt{5}$

    $e = -4 + \sqrt{5}$ or $e = -4 - \sqrt{5}$

(c) $36m^2 - 84m + 46 = 0$

   $(6m)^2 - 84m + 49 = 3$

    $(6m - 7)^2 = 3$

  $6m - 7 = \sqrt{3}$ or $6m - 7 = -\sqrt{3}$

    $6m = 7 + \sqrt{3}$ or $6m = 7 - \sqrt{3}$

     $m = \dfrac{7 + \sqrt{3}}{6}$ or $m = \dfrac{7 - \sqrt{3}}{6}$

We can express any quadratic equation in the form $ax^2 + bx + c = 0$.
If we solved this equation by completing the square, the result would be:

$$x = \frac{-b \pm \sqrt{b^2 - 4ac}}{2a}$$

This is called the **quadratic formula**.
We use it as a formula for solving quadratic equations when we can't factorise the trinomial.

Example:
Use the quadratic formula to solve the equation $2x^2 + 7x + 4 = 0$.

Solution:

$2x^2 + 7x + 4 = 0$	Write down the equation.
$a = 2, \quad b = 7, \quad c = 4$	Write down the values of a, b and c.
$x = \dfrac{-b \pm \sqrt{b^2 - 4ac}}{2a}$	Write down the formula.
$= \dfrac{-7 \pm \sqrt{7^2 - 4 \times 2 \times 4}}{2 \times 2}$	Substitute the values of a, b and c.
$= \dfrac{-7 \pm \sqrt{49 - 32}}{4}$	Work out the answer.
$= \dfrac{-7 \pm \sqrt{17}}{4}$	Notice that there are two values for x.
$x = \dfrac{-7 + \sqrt{17}}{4} \quad \text{or} \quad x = \dfrac{-7 - \sqrt{17}}{4}$	We can leave the answer as it is above or write the two answers out separately.

In the formula, a is the coefficient of x^2, b is the coefficient of x, and c is the constant term (the number at the end). If terms are subtracted, the values of b or c could be negative.

Example:
Solve, leaving the answers in surd form: (a) $x^2 - 9x - 13 = 0$ (b) $4x^2 + 7x + 1 = 0$

Solution:

(a) $x^2 - 9x - 13 = 0$
$a = 1, \quad b = -9, \quad c = -13$

$$x = \frac{-b \pm \sqrt{b^2 - 4ac}}{2a}$$

$$= \frac{-(-9) \pm \sqrt{(-9)^2 - 4 \times 1 \times -13}}{2 \times 1}$$

$$= \frac{9 \pm \sqrt{133}}{2}$$

$$x = \frac{9 + \sqrt{133}}{2} \quad \text{or} \quad x = \frac{9 - \sqrt{133}}{2}$$

(b) $4x^2 + 7x + 1 = 0$
$a = 4, \quad b = 7, \quad c = 1$

$$x = \frac{-b \pm \sqrt{b^2 - 4ac}}{2a}$$

$$= \frac{-7 \pm \sqrt{7^2 - 4 \times 4 \times 1}}{2 \times 4}$$

$$= \frac{-7 \pm \sqrt{33}}{8}$$

$$x = \frac{-7 + \sqrt{33}}{8} \quad \text{or} \quad x = \frac{-7 - \sqrt{33}}{8}$$

1. Use the quadratic formula to solve:

(a) $2x^2 + 9x + 3 = 0$

(b) $3x^2 + 7x - 2 = 0$

(c) $x^2 + 5x + 3 = 0$

(d) $5x^2 - 5x + 1 = 0$

(e) $2x^2 - 3x - 7 = 0$

(f) $4x^2 + 11x + 2 = 0$

(g) $x^2 - 7x - 4 = 0$

(h) $7x^2 + x - 3 = 0$

(i) $8x^2 - 3x - 5 = 0$

THE QUADRATIC FORMULA Worked Solutions

1. Use the quadratic formula to solve:

(a) $2x^2 + 9x + 3 = 0$ .... ☞ Write down the equation,

$a = 2, \quad b = 9, \quad c = 3$ and the values of a, b and c.

$x = \dfrac{-b \pm \sqrt{b^2 - 4ac}}{2a}$ .... ☞ Write the formula.

$= \dfrac{-9 \pm \sqrt{9^2 - 4 \times 2 \times 3}}{2 \times 2}$ .... ☞ Substitute the values of a, b and c.

$= \dfrac{-9 \pm \sqrt{57}}{4}$ .... ☞ OR $x = \dfrac{-9 + \sqrt{57}}{4}$ or $x = \dfrac{-9 - \sqrt{57}}{4}$

(b) $3x^2 + 7x - 2 = 0$

$a = 3, \quad b = 7, \quad c = -2$ .... ☞ c must be negative.

$x = \dfrac{-b \pm \sqrt{b^2 - 4ac}}{2a}$ .... ☞ Write the formula.

$= \dfrac{-7 \pm \sqrt{7^2 - 4 \times 3 \times -2}}{2 \times 3}$ .... ☞ Substitute the values of a, b and c.

$= \dfrac{-7 \pm \sqrt{73}}{6}$ .... ☞ OR $x = \dfrac{-7 + \sqrt{73}}{6}$ or $x = \dfrac{-7 - \sqrt{73}}{6}$

(c) $x^2 + 5x + 3 = 0$

$a = 1, \quad b = 5, \quad c = 3$ .... ☞ x^2 means $1x^2$ so the value of a is 1.

$x = \dfrac{-b \pm \sqrt{b^2 - 4ac}}{2a}$ .... ☞ Write the formula.

$= \dfrac{-5 \pm \sqrt{5^2 - 4 \times 1 \times 3}}{2 \times 1}$ .... ☞ Substitute the values of a, b and c.

$= \dfrac{5 \pm \sqrt{13}}{2}$ .... ☞ OR $x = \dfrac{-5 + \sqrt{13}}{2}$ or $x = \dfrac{-5 - \sqrt{13}}{2}$

(d) $5x^2 - 5x + 1 = 0$

$a = 5, \quad b = -5, \quad c = 1$

$x = \dfrac{-b \pm \sqrt{b^2 - 4ac}}{2a}$ .... ☞ Write the formula.

$= \dfrac{-(-5) \pm \sqrt{(-5)^2 - 4 \times 5 \times 1}}{2 \times 5}$ .... ☞ Be careful with the negative value of b.

$= \dfrac{5 \pm \sqrt{5}}{10}$ .... ☞ OR $x = \dfrac{5 + \sqrt{5}}{10}$ or $x = \dfrac{5 - \sqrt{5}}{10}$

(e) $2x^2 - 3x - 7 = 0$

$a = 2, \quad b = -3, \quad c = -7$ .... ☞ Both b and c are negative.

$x = \dfrac{-b \pm \sqrt{b^2 - 4ac}}{2a}$ .... ☞ Write the formula.

$= \dfrac{-(-3) \pm \sqrt{(-3)^2 - 4 \times 2 \times -7}}{2 \times 2}$ .... ☞ Substitute the values of a, b and c.

$= \dfrac{3 \pm \sqrt{65}}{4}$ .... ☞ OR $x = \dfrac{3 + \sqrt{65}}{4}$ or $x = \dfrac{3 - \sqrt{65}}{4}$

(f) $4x^2 + 11x + 2 = 0$
$a = 4, \quad b = 11, \quad c = 2$

$x = \dfrac{-b \pm \sqrt{b^2 - 4ac}}{2a}$ .... ☞ Write the formula.

$= \dfrac{-11 \pm \sqrt{11^2 - 4 \times 4 \times 2}}{2 \times 4}$

$= \dfrac{-11 \pm \sqrt{89}}{8}$ .... ☞ OR $\;x = \dfrac{-11 + \sqrt{89}}{8}\;$ or $\;x = \dfrac{-11 - \sqrt{89}}{8}$

(g) $x^2 - 7x - 4 = 0$
$a = 1, \quad b = -7, \quad c = -4$

$x = \dfrac{-b \pm \sqrt{b^2 - 4ac}}{2a}$ .... ☞ Write the formula.

$= \dfrac{-(-7) \pm \sqrt{(-7)^2 - 4 \times 1 \times -4}}{2 \times 1}$ .... ☞ Substitute the values of a, b and c.

$= \dfrac{7 \pm \sqrt{65}}{2}$

(h) $7x^2 + x - 3 = 0$
$a = 7, \quad b = 1, \quad c = -3$

$x = \dfrac{-b \pm \sqrt{b^2 - 4ac}}{2a}$ .... ☞ Write the formula.

$= \dfrac{-1 \pm \sqrt{1^2 - 4 \times 7 \times -3}}{2 \times 7}$

$= \dfrac{-1 \pm \sqrt{85}}{14}$

(i) $8x^2 - 3x - 5 = 0$
$a = 8, \quad b = -3, \quad c = -5$

$x = \dfrac{-b \pm \sqrt{b^2 - 4ac}}{2a}$ .... ☞ Write the formula.

$= \dfrac{-(-3) \pm \sqrt{(-3)^2 - 4 \times 8 \times -5}}{2 \times 8}$ .... ☞ Substitute the values of a, b and c.

$= \dfrac{3 \pm \sqrt{169}}{16}$ .... ☞ Because $\sqrt{169} = 13$ we can simplify this answer.

$= \dfrac{3 \pm 13}{16}$

$x = \dfrac{16}{16}\;$ or $\;x = -\dfrac{10}{16}$

$x = 1\;$ or $\;x = -\dfrac{5}{8}$ .... ☞ We could also solve this equation by factorising.

THE QUADRATIC FORMULA AND DECIMAL APPROXIMATIONS Summary

> If we want the exact answer to a quadratic equation, we might need to leave the answer as a surd, but it is often more useful to have a decimal approximation to the solution.

Example:
Solve the quadratic equation $5x^2 - 6x - 2 = 0$, giving each answer correct to 3 decimal places.

Solution:

$5x^2 - 6x - 2 = 0$ We begin just like any other use of the formula.
$a = 5, \quad b = -6, \quad c = -2$

$x = \dfrac{-b \pm \sqrt{b^2 - 4ac}}{2a}$ Always write the formula.

$= \dfrac{-(-6) \pm \sqrt{(-6)^2 - 4 \times 5 \times -2}}{2 \times 5}$

$= \dfrac{6 \pm \sqrt{36+40}}{10}$

$= \dfrac{6 \pm \sqrt{76}}{10}$

$x = \dfrac{6 + \sqrt{76}}{10} \quad \text{or} \quad x = \dfrac{6 - \sqrt{76}}{10}$

$x = 1.471779789 \quad \text{or} \quad x = -0.271779788$ [by calculator]
$x = 1.472 \qquad \text{or} \qquad x = -0.272$ [correct to 3 decimal places]

> Different calculators do this in slightly different ways.
> Make sure you can use **your** calculator to get the right answer.

Example:
Solve these quadratic equations, giving the answers correct to 3 decimal places:
(a) $2x^2 + 5x + 1 = 0$ (b) $3x^2 - 8x + 2 = 0$

Solution:

(a) $2x^2 + 5x + 1 = 0$

$a = 2, \quad b = 5, \quad c = 1$

$x = \dfrac{-b \pm \sqrt{b^2 - 4ac}}{2a}$

$= \dfrac{-5 \pm \sqrt{5^2 - 4 \times 2 \times 1}}{2 \times 2}$

$= \dfrac{-5 \pm \sqrt{25 - 8}}{4}$

$= \dfrac{-5 \pm \sqrt{17}}{4}$

$x = \dfrac{-5 + \sqrt{17}}{4} \quad \text{or} \quad x = \dfrac{-5 - \sqrt{17}}{4}$

$x = -0.219223593 \text{ or } x = -2.280776406$
[by calculator]
$x = -0.219 \qquad \text{or} \quad x = -2.281$
[correct to 3 decimal places]

(b) $3x^2 - 8x + 2 = 0$

$a = 3, \quad b = -8, \quad c = 2$

$x = \dfrac{-b \pm \sqrt{b^2 - 4ac}}{2a}$

$= \dfrac{-(-8) \pm \sqrt{(-8^2) - 4 \times 3 \times 2}}{2 \times 3}$

$= \dfrac{8 \pm \sqrt{64 - 24}}{6}$

$= \dfrac{8 \pm \sqrt{40}}{6}$

$x = \dfrac{8 + \sqrt{40}}{6} \quad \text{or} \quad x = \dfrac{8 - \sqrt{40}}{6}$

$x = 2.387425887 \text{ or } x = 0.279240779$
[by calculator]
$x = 2.387 \qquad \text{or} \quad x = 0.279$
[correct to 3 decimal places]

1. Solve these quadratic equations, giving each answer correct to three decimal places:

(a) $2x^2 + 7x + 1 = 0$

(b) $3x^2 - 11x + 2 = 0$

(c) $6x^2 - 2x - 5 = 0$

(d) $x^2 - 5x - 1 = 0$

(e) $5x^2 + 6x - 2 = 0$

(f) $2x^2 - 9x - 7 = 0$

(g) $7x^2 + 2x - 3 = 0$

(h) $3x^2 + 7x + 3 = 0$

(i) $4x^2 - 11x + 5 = 0$

THE QUADRATIC FORMULA AND DECIMALS Worked Solutions

1. Solve these quadratic equations, giving each answer correct to three decimal places:

(a) $2x^2 + 7x + 1 = 0$ .... ☞ Write down the equation,
$a = 2, \quad b = 7, \quad c = 1$ and the values of a, b and c.

$x = \dfrac{-b \pm \sqrt{b^2 - 4ac}}{2a}$ .... ☞ Write the formula.

$= \dfrac{-7 \pm \sqrt{7^2 - 4 \times 2 \times 1}}{2 \times 2}$ .... ☞ Substitute the values of a, b and c.

$= \dfrac{-7 \pm \sqrt{41}}{4}$

$x = \dfrac{-7 + \sqrt{41}}{4}$ or $\quad x = \dfrac{-7 - \sqrt{41}}{4}$

$x = -0.14921894$ or $\quad x = -3.350781059$
[by calculator]

$x = -0.149$ or $\quad x = -3.351$ .... ☞ Be careful to round off correctly.
[correct to 3 decimal places]

(b) $3x^2 - 11x + 2 = 0$
$a = 3, \quad b = -11, \quad c = 2$

$x = \dfrac{-b \pm \sqrt{b^2 - 4ac}}{2a}$ .... ☞ Write the formula.

$= \dfrac{-(-11) \pm \sqrt{(-11)^2 - 4 \times 3 \times 2}}{2 \times 3}$ .... ☞ Take care with the negative value of b.

$= \dfrac{11 \pm \sqrt{97}}{6}$

$x = \dfrac{11 + \sqrt{97}}{6}$ or $\quad x = \dfrac{11 - \sqrt{97}}{6}$

$x = 3.474809634$ or $x = 0.191857033$ [by calculator]
$x = 3.475$ or $\quad x = 0.192$ [correct to 3 decimal places]

(c) $6x^2 - 2x - 5 = 0$
$a = 6, \quad b = -2, \quad c = -5$

$x = \dfrac{-b \pm \sqrt{b^2 - 4ac}}{2a}$

$= \dfrac{-(-2) \pm \sqrt{(-2)^2 - 4 \times 6 \times -5}}{2 \times 6}$

$= \dfrac{2 \pm \sqrt{124}}{12}$

$x = \dfrac{2 + \sqrt{124}}{12}$ or $\quad x = \dfrac{2 - \sqrt{124}}{12}$

$x = 1.094627394$ or $x = -0.76129406$
[by calculator]
$x = 1.095$ or $\quad x = -0.761$
[correct to 3 decimal places]

(d) $x^2 - 5x - 1 = 0$
$a = 1, \quad b = -5, \quad c = -1$

$x = \dfrac{-b \pm \sqrt{b^2 - 4ac}}{2a}$

$= \dfrac{-(-5) \pm \sqrt{(-5)^2 - 4 \times 1 \times -1}}{2 \times 1}$

$= \dfrac{5 \pm \sqrt{29}}{2}$

$x = \dfrac{5 + \sqrt{29}}{2}$ or $\quad x = \dfrac{5 - \sqrt{29}}{2}$

$x = 5.192582404$ or $x = -0.192582403$
[by calculator]
$x = 5.193$ or $\quad x = -0.193$
[correct to 3 decimal places]

(e) $5x^2 + 6x - 2 = 0$

$a = 5, \quad b = 6, \quad c = -2$

$x = \dfrac{-b \pm \sqrt{b^2 - 4ac}}{2a}$ ☞ Write the formula.

$= \dfrac{-6 \pm \sqrt{6^2 - 4 \times 5 \times -2}}{2 \times 5}$ ☞ Substitute the values of a, b and c.

$= \dfrac{-6 \pm \sqrt{76}}{10}$

$x = \dfrac{-6 + \sqrt{76}}{10} \quad$ or $\quad x = \dfrac{-6 - \sqrt{76}}{10}$ ☞ Evaluate using a calculator.

$x = 0.271779788 \quad$ or $\quad x = -1.471779789$

[by calculator]

$x = 0.272 \quad$ or $\qquad x = -1.472$

[correct to 3 decimal places]

(f) $2x^2 - 9x - 7 = 0$

$a = 2, \quad b = -9, \quad c = -7$

$x = \dfrac{-b \pm \sqrt{b^2 - 4ac}}{2a}$

$= \dfrac{-(-9) \pm \sqrt{(-9)^2 - 4 \times 2 \times -7}}{2 \times 2}$

$= \dfrac{9 \pm \sqrt{137}}{4}$

$x = \dfrac{9 + \sqrt{137}}{4} \quad$ or $\quad x = \dfrac{9 - \sqrt{137}}{4}$

$x = 5.176174978 \quad$ or $\quad x = -0.676174977$

[by calculator]

$x = 5.176 \quad$ or $\qquad x = -0.676$

[correct to 3 decimal places]

(g) $7x^2 + 2x - 3 = 0$

$a = 7, \quad b = 2, \quad c = -3$

$x = \dfrac{-b \pm \sqrt{b^2 - 4ac}}{2a}$

$= \dfrac{-2 \pm \sqrt{2^2 - 4 \times 7 \times -3}}{2 \times 7}$

$= \dfrac{-2 \pm \sqrt{88}}{14}$

$x = \dfrac{-2 + \sqrt{88}}{14} \quad$ or $\quad x = \dfrac{-2 - \sqrt{88}}{14}$

$x = 0.527202251 \quad$ or $\quad x = -0.812916537$

[by calculator]

$x = 0.527 \quad$ or $\qquad x = -0.813$

[correct to 3 decimal places]

(h) $3x^2 + 7x + 3 = 0$

$a = 3, \quad b = 7, \quad c = 3$

$x = \dfrac{-b \pm \sqrt{b^2 - 4ac}}{2a}$

$= \dfrac{-7 \pm \sqrt{7^2 - 4 \times 3 \times 3}}{2 \times 3}$

$= \dfrac{-7 \pm \sqrt{13}}{6}$

$x = \dfrac{-7 + \sqrt{13}}{6} \quad$ or $\quad x = \dfrac{-7 - \sqrt{13}}{6}$

$x = -0.565741454 \quad$ or $\quad x = -1.767591879$

[by calculator]

$x = -0.566 \quad$ or $\qquad x = -1.768$

[correct to 3 decimal places]

(i) $4x^2 - 11x + 5 = 0$

$a = 4, \quad b = -11, \quad c = 5$

$x = \dfrac{-b \pm \sqrt{b^2 - 4ac}}{2a}$

$= \dfrac{-(-11) \pm \sqrt{(-11)^2 - 4 \times 4 \times 5}}{2 \times 4}$

$= \dfrac{11 \pm \sqrt{41}}{8}$

$x = \dfrac{11 + \sqrt{41}}{8} \quad$ or $\quad x = \dfrac{11 - \sqrt{41}}{8}$

$x = 2.17539053 \quad$ or $\quad x = 0.57460947$

[by calculator]

$x = 2.175 \quad$ or $\qquad x = 0.575$

[correct to 3 decimal places]

We have three different methods of solving quadratic equations.

Factorise, if possible;

Remember: First make sure the quadratic equation is equal to zero.

OR complete the square.

OR use the quadratic formula.

Example:

Solve: (a) $x^2 + 8x = 9$ (b) $x^2 - 16x + 5 = 0$ (c) $3x^2 + 2x - 8 = 0$ (d) $x^2 + 3x - 7 = 0$

Solution:

(a)
$$x^2 + 8x = 9$$
$$x^2 + 8x - 9 = 0$$
$$(x + 9)(x - 1) = 0$$
$$x + 9 = 0 \quad \text{or} \quad x - 1 = 0$$
$$x = -9 \quad \text{or} \quad x = 1$$

(b)
$$x^2 - 16x + 5 = 0$$
$$x^2 - 16x + 64 = 59$$
$$(x - 8)^2 = 59$$
$$x - 8 = \sqrt{59} \quad \text{or} \quad x - 8 = -\sqrt{59}$$
$$x = 8 + \sqrt{59} \quad \text{or} \quad x = 8 - \sqrt{59}$$

(c)
$$3x^2 + 2x - 8 = 0$$
$$(3x - 4)(x + 2) = 0$$
$$3x - 4 = 0 \quad \text{or} \quad x + 2 = 0$$
$$3x = 4 \quad \text{or} \quad x = -2$$
$$x = 1\tfrac{1}{3} \quad \text{or} \quad x = -2$$

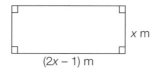

$$3x \times 2 + x \times -4 = 2x \checkmark$$

(d)
$$x^2 + 3x - 7 = 0$$
$$a = 1, \quad b = 3, \quad c = -7$$
$$x = \frac{-b \pm \sqrt{b^2 - 4ac}}{2a}$$
$$= \frac{-3 \pm \sqrt{3^2 - 4 \times 1 \times -7}}{2 \times 1}$$
$$= \frac{-3 \pm \sqrt{37}}{2}$$

Some practical problems can be solved by finding the solution to a quadratic equation.

Example:

A rectangle has an area of 15 m². The length is 1 m less than twice the breadth. What are the dimensions of the rectangle?

Solution:

Let the breadth of the rectangle be x metres.

Length = twice the breadth less 1 metre

$\therefore$ Length = $(2x - 1)$ metres.

x m

$(2x - 1)$ m

Area = 15 m²

$$\therefore x(2x - 1) = 15$$
$$2x^2 - x = 15$$
$$2x^2 - x - 15 = 0$$
$$(2x + 5)(x - 3) = 0$$
$$2x + 5 = 0 \quad \text{or} \quad x - 3 = 0$$
$$2x = -5 \quad \text{or} \quad x = 3$$
$$x = -2.5 \quad \text{or} \quad x = 3$$

But the breadth of the rectangle cannot be negative.

$\therefore$ **Breadth = 3 metres**

Length = 2 × 3 − 1

= 5 metres

$\therefore$ **The rectangle is 5 m long and 3 m wide.**

$$2x \times -3 + x \times 5 = -x \checkmark$$

1. **Solve by factorising:**

   (a) $x^2 - 11x + 30 = 0$

   (b) $a^2 + 3a - 10 = 0$

   (c) $p^2 - 4p - 45 = 0$

   (d) $3x^2 + 19x + 20 = 0$

   (e) $12x^2 + 7x - 12 = 0$

2. **Solve by completing the square:**

   (a) $a^2 + 22a = -119$

   (b) $n^2 - 8n + 13 = 0$

   (c) $k^2 + 6k + 7 = 3$

3. **Solve using the quadratic formula (giving the answers to (b) and (c) correct to three decimal places):**

   (a) $x^2 - 7x + 2 = 0$

   (b) $3x^2 + 5x - 4 = 0$

   (c) $2x^2 - 3x - 11 = 0$

4. A rectangle has an area of 72 cm². The length is 6 cm longer than the breadth. Form a quadratic equation and solve it to find the dimensions of the rectangle.

5. The product of two consecutive numbers is 56. Form a quadratic equation and solve it to find all possible such numbers.

1. Solve by factorising:

   (a) $x^2 - 11x + 30 = 0$ .... ☞ We have a trinomial to factorise.
   $(x - 6)(x - 5) = 0$
   $x - 6 = 0$ or $x - 5 = 0$
   $x = 6$ or $x = 5$

   What 2 numbers add to -11 and multiply to 30?
   One of the terms in the product must be zero.

   (b) $a^2 + 3a - 10 = 0$
   $(a + 5)(a - 2) = 0$
   $a + 5 = 0$ or $a - 2 = 0$
   $a = -5$ or $a = 2$

   (c) $p^2 - 4p - 45 = 0$
   $(p - 9)(p + 5) = 0$
   $p - 9 = 0$ or $p + 5 = 0$
   $p = 9$ or $p = -5$

   (d) $3x^2 + 19x + 20 = 0$ .... ☞ Using the cross method to factorise.
   $(3x + 4)(x + 5) = 0$
   $3x + 4 = 0$ or $x + 5 = 0$
   $3x = -4$ or $x = -5$
   $x = -1\frac{1}{3}$ or $x = -5$

   $3x$ ⤬ $+4$
   x $+5$
   $3x \times 5 + x \times 4 = 19x$ ✓

   (e) $12x^2 + 7x - 12 = 0$
   $(4x - 3)(3x + 4) = 0$
   $4x - 3 = 0$ or $3x + 4 = 0$
   $4x = 3$ or $3x = -4$
   $x = \frac{3}{4}$ or $x = -1\frac{1}{3}$

   $4x$ ⤬ -3
   $3x$ $+4$
   $4x \times 4 + 3x \times -3 = 7x$ ✓

2. Solve by completing the square:

   (a) $a^2 + 22a = -119$ .... ☞ $a^2 + 22a = a^2 + 2 \times a \times 11$
   $a^2 + 22a + 121 = -119 + 121$
   $(a + 11)^2 = 2$
   $a + 11 = \sqrt{2}$ or $a + 11 = -\sqrt{2}$
   $a = -11 + \sqrt{2}$ or $a = -11 - \sqrt{2}$

   Add 11^2 to both sides of the equation.

   (b) $n^2 - 8n + 13 = 0$
   $n^2 - 8n + 16 = 3$
   $(n - 4)^2 = 3$
   $n - 4 = \sqrt{3}$ or $n - 4 = -\sqrt{3}$
   $n = 4 + \sqrt{3}$ or $n = 4 - \sqrt{3}$

   (c) $k^2 + 6k + 7 = 3$
   $k^2 + 6k + 9 = 5$
   $(k + 3)^2 = 5$
   $k + 3 = \sqrt{5}$ or $k + 3 = -\sqrt{5}$
   $k = -3 + \sqrt{5}$ or $k = -3 - \sqrt{5}$

3. Solve using the quadratic formula (giving the answers to (b) and (c) correct to three decimal places):

   (a) $x^2 - 7x + 2 = 0$
   $a = 1,\ b = -7,\ c = 2$ .... ☞ Write down the values of a, b and c.

   $x = \dfrac{-b \pm \sqrt{b^2 - 4ac}}{2a}$ Write the formula.

   $= \dfrac{-(-7) \pm \sqrt{(-7)^2 - 4 \times 1 \times 2}}{2 \times 1}$ Substitute the values of a, b and c.

   $x = \dfrac{7 + \sqrt{41}}{2}$

(b) $3x^2 + 5x - 4 = 0$
$a = 3, \quad b = 5, \quad c = -4$

$x = \dfrac{-b \pm \sqrt{b^2 - 4ac}}{2a}$

$= \dfrac{-5 \pm \sqrt{5^2 - 4 \times 3 \times -4}}{2 \times 3}$

$= \dfrac{-5 \pm \sqrt{73}}{6}$

$x = \dfrac{-5 + \sqrt{73}}{6} \quad$ or $\quad x = \dfrac{-5 - \sqrt{73}}{6}$

$x = 0.59066729$ or $x = -2.257333958$
[by calculator]

$x = 0.591 \qquad$ or $\quad x = -2.257$
[correct to 3 decimal places]

(c) $2x^2 - 3x - 11 = 0$
$a = 2, \quad b = -3, \quad c = -11$

$x = \dfrac{-b \pm \sqrt{b^2 - 4ac}}{2a}$

$= \dfrac{-(-3) \pm \sqrt{(-3)^2 - 4 \times 2 \times -11}}{2 \times 2}$

$= \dfrac{3 \pm \sqrt{97}}{4}$

$x = \dfrac{3 + \sqrt{97}}{4} \quad$ or $\quad x = \dfrac{3 - \sqrt{97}}{4}$

$x = 3.21221445$ or $x = -1.71221445$
[by calculator]

$x = 3.212 \qquad$ or $\quad x = -1.712$
[correct to 3 decimal places]

4. A rectangle has an area of 72 cm². The length is 6 cm longer than the breadth. Form a quadratic equation and solve it to find the dimensions of the rectangle.

Let the breadth be b cm.
∴ The length is $(b + 6)$ cm
Area $= 72$ cm²
∴ $\qquad b(b + 6) = 72$
$\qquad b^2 + 6b = 72$
$\qquad b^2 + 6b - 72 = 0$
$\qquad (b + 12)(b - 6) = 0$
$\qquad b + 12 = 0 \quad$ or $\quad b - 6 = 0$
$\qquad b = -12 \quad$ or $\quad b = 6$
But $b > 0, \quad ∴ \quad b = 6$ ☞ The breadth cannot be negative.
Length $= 6 + 6$
$\qquad = 12$ cm
∴ **The rectangle is 12 cm long and 6 cm wide.** ☞ Answer with a statement.

5. The product of two consecutive numbers is 56. Form a quadratic equation and solve it to find all possible such numbers.

Let the first number be x. ☞ Begin with a statement like this.
∴ The second number is $x + 1$ ☞ The numbers are consecutive.
$\qquad x(x + 1) = 56$ ☞ The product of the numbers is 56.
$\qquad x^2 + x = 56$
$\qquad x^2 + x - 56 = 0$ ☞ Set the equation equal to zero.
$\qquad (x + 8)(x - 7) = 0$ Factorise,
$\qquad x + 8 = 0 \quad$ or $\quad x - 7 = 0$ and solve.
$\qquad x = -8 \quad$ or $\quad x = 7$
The first number is -8 or 7.
The second number is $-8 + 1 = -7$ or $7 + 1 = 8$.
∴ **The two numbers are -8 and -7 or 7 and 8.**

FRACTIONAL INDICES Summary

> We know that $8^2 = 64$, so $\sqrt{64} = 8$.
> Similarly, we know that $(x^5)^2 = x^{10}$, (we multiply the indices), so $\sqrt{x^{10}} = x^5$.
> To square a power we multiply the index by 2. To find the square root of a power
> we divide the index by 2, or halve the index.

Example:
Find: (a) $\sqrt{m^{16}}$ (b) $\sqrt{k^{12}}$ (c) $\sqrt{9e^6}$ (d) $\sqrt{64n^{64}}$ (e) $\sqrt{p^4q^6}$ (f) $\sqrt{y^2}$

Solution:
(a) $\sqrt{m^{16}} = m^8$ (b) $\sqrt{k^{12}} = k^6$ (c) $\sqrt{9e^6} = 3e^3 \left[\sqrt{9e^6} = \sqrt{9} \times \sqrt{e^6} \right]$

(d) $\sqrt{64n^{64}} = 8n^{32}$ (e) $\sqrt{p^4q^6} = p^2q^3$ (f) $\sqrt{y^2} = y$ $[y^1]$

Using the index rules, $(x^{\frac{1}{2}})^2 = x$ so $\sqrt{x} = x^{\frac{1}{2}}$

$(x^{\frac{1}{3}})^3 = x$ so $\sqrt[3]{x} = x^{\frac{1}{3}}$

$(x^{\frac{1}{4}})^4 = x$ so $\sqrt[4]{x} = x^{\frac{1}{4}}$

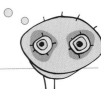

$x^{\frac{1}{2}} = \sqrt{x}$
$x^{\frac{1}{n}} = \sqrt[n]{x}$

Example:
Write in index form: (a) $\sqrt{t}$ (b) $\sqrt[4]{d}$ (c) $\sqrt[3]{z}$ (d) $\sqrt[8]{pq}$

Solution:
(a) $\sqrt{t} = t^{\frac{1}{2}}$ (b) $\sqrt[4]{d} = d^{\frac{1}{4}}$ (c) $\sqrt[3]{z} = z^{\frac{1}{3}}$ (d) $\sqrt[8]{pq} = (pq)^{\frac{1}{8}}$

Example:
Write without indices: (a) $m^{\frac{1}{5}}$ (b) $t^{\frac{1}{6}}$ (c) $(9n)^{\frac{1}{2}}$ (d) $4a^{\frac{1}{2}}$

Solution:
(a) $m^{\frac{1}{5}} = \sqrt[5]{m}$ (b) $t^{\frac{1}{6}} = \sqrt[6]{t}$ (c) $(9n)^{\frac{1}{2}} = \sqrt{9n}$ (d) $4a^{\frac{1}{2}} = 4 \times a^{\frac{1}{2}}$

$= \sqrt{9} \times \sqrt{n}$ $= 4 \times \sqrt{a}$

$= 3\sqrt{n}$ $= 4\sqrt{a}$

> $(x^{\frac{1}{3}})^2 = x^{\frac{2}{3}}$ by the index rules, but $(x^{\frac{1}{3}})^2 = (\sqrt[3]{x})^2$
> $$x^{\frac{m}{n}} = \sqrt[n]{x^m} = (\sqrt[n]{x})^m$$

Example:
Write in index form: (a) $\sqrt[3]{a^2}$ (b) $\sqrt[4]{x^5}$ (c) $\sqrt{n^3}$ (d) $(\sqrt{u})^9$

Solution:
(a) $\sqrt[3]{a^2} = a^{\frac{2}{3}}$ (b) $\sqrt[4]{x^5} = x^{\frac{5}{4}}$ (c) $\sqrt{n^3} = n^{\frac{3}{2}}$ (d) $(\sqrt{u})^9 = u^{\frac{9}{2}}$

Example:
Write without fractional indices: (a) $e^{\frac{3}{4}}$ (b) $z^{\frac{7}{2}}$ (c) $2c^{\frac{4}{5}}$ (d) $(8h)^{\frac{2}{3}}$

Solution:
(a) $e^{\frac{3}{4}} = \sqrt[4]{e^3}$ (b) $z^{\frac{7}{2}} = \sqrt{z^7}$ (c) $2c^{\frac{4}{5}} = 2 \times c^{\frac{4}{5}}$ (d) $(8h)^{\frac{2}{3}} = (\sqrt[3]{8h})^2$

$= 2(\sqrt[5]{c})^4$ $= \sqrt[3]{8^2} \times \sqrt[3]{h^2}$

$= 4\sqrt[3]{h^2}$

1 Find:

(a) $\sqrt{a^8}$ = _____

(b) $\sqrt{n^{36}}$ = _____

(c) $\sqrt{x^{18}}$ = _____

(d) $\sqrt{u^{24}}$ = _____

(e) $\sqrt{p^4}$ = _____

(f) $\sqrt{m^{14}}$ = _____

(g) $\sqrt{g^{100}}$ = _____

(h) $\sqrt{c^2}$ = _____

(i) $\sqrt{16b^{16}}$ = _____

(j) $\sqrt{36z^{10}}$ = _____

(k) $\sqrt{9q^{64}}$ = _____

(l) $\sqrt{a^8b^{12}}$ = _____

2. Write in index form:

(a) $\sqrt{u}$ = _____

(b) $\sqrt{y}$ = _____

(c) $\sqrt[5]{e}$ = _____

(d) $\sqrt[6]{k}$ = _____

(e) $\sqrt[3]{ab}$ = _____

(f) $\sqrt{7a}$ = _____

3. Write without indices:

(a) $h^{\frac{1}{2}}$ = _____

(b) $p^{\frac{1}{4}}$ = _____

(c) $t^{\frac{1}{8}}$ = _____

(d) $(xy)^{\frac{1}{2}}$ = _____

(e) $(100g)^{\frac{1}{2}}$ = _____

(f) $25e^{\frac{1}{2}}$ = _____

= _____

= _____

= _____

= _____

= _____

= _____

4. Write in index form:

(a) $\sqrt[4]{a^3}$ = _____

(b) $\sqrt[3]{y^4}$ = _____

(c) $\sqrt{x^7}$ = _____

(d) $(\sqrt[3]{p})^8$ = _____

(e) $(\sqrt{w})^5$ = _____

(f) $(\sqrt[5]{mn})^2$ = _____

5. Write without fractional indices:

(a) $d^{\frac{3}{2}}$ = _____

(b) $x^{\frac{4}{5}}$ = _____

(c) $(yz)^{\frac{5}{6}}$ = _____

(d) $(4a)^{\frac{1}{2}}$ = _____

(e) $(27e)^{\frac{1}{3}}$ = _____

(f) $(16m)^{\frac{3}{4}}$ = _____

= _____

= _____

= _____

= _____

= _____

= _____

6. Given $x = 25$, $y = 27$ and $z = 16$, find:

(a) $x^{\frac{1}{2}}$ = _____

(b) $z^{\frac{1}{4}}$ = _____

(c) $y^{\frac{2}{3}}$ = _____

= _____

= _____

= _____

= _____

= _____

= _____

7. Simplify:

(a) $(u^{16})^{\frac{1}{2}}$ = _____

(b) $(n^8)^{\frac{3}{4}}$ = _____

(c) $(9a^6)^{\frac{1}{2}}$ = _____

(d) $2m^{\frac{1}{2}} \times 3m^{\frac{1}{2}}$ = _____

(e) $20h^{\frac{3}{4}} \div 4h^{\frac{1}{2}}$ = _____

= _____

= _____

FRACTIONAL INDICES Worked Solutions

1. Find:

   (a) $\sqrt{a^8} = a^4$ .... ☞ To take the square root, halve the index.

   (b) $\sqrt{n^{36}} = n^{18}$ .... ☞ $\frac{1}{2}$ of 36 is 18.

   (c) $\sqrt{x^{18}} = x^9$ .... ☞ Halve the index.

   (d) $\sqrt{u^{24}} = u^{12}$

   (e) $\sqrt{p^4} = p^2$

   (f) $\sqrt{m^{14}} = m^7$

   (g) $\sqrt{g^{100}} = g^{50}$ .... ☞ It is not g^{10}. Don't take the square root of the index.

   (h) $\sqrt{c^2} = c$ .... ☞ c^1 but we don't need to write the one.

   (i) $\sqrt{16b^{16}} = 4b^8$ .... ☞ $\sqrt{16} = 4$. We still take the square root of any number (that is not an index).

   (j) $\sqrt{36z^{10}} = 6z^5$ .... ☞ $\sqrt{36} = 6$, $\frac{1}{2}$ of 10 = 5.

   (k) $\sqrt{9q^{64}} = 3q^{32}$

   (l) $\sqrt{a^8 b^{12}} = a^4 b^6$ .... ☞ Halve the indices, separately for each pronumeral.

2. Write in index form:

   (a) $\sqrt{u} = u^{\frac{1}{2}}$ .... ☞ The square root is a power of a half.

   (b) $\sqrt{y} = y^{\frac{1}{2}}$

   (c) $\sqrt[5]{e} = e^{\frac{1}{5}}$ .... ☞ The fifth root is the power of one-fifth.

   (d) $\sqrt[6]{k} = k^{\frac{1}{6}}$

   (e) $\sqrt[3]{ab} = (ab)^{\frac{1}{3}}$

   (f) $\sqrt{7a} = (7a)^{\frac{1}{2}}$

3. Write without indices:

   (a) $h^{\frac{1}{2}} = \sqrt{h}$ .... ☞ A power of a half means the square root.

   (b) $p^{\frac{1}{4}} = \sqrt[4]{p}$

   (c) $t^{\frac{1}{8}} = \sqrt[8]{t}$

   (d) $(xy)^{\frac{1}{2}} = \sqrt{xy}$ .... ☞ The square root of everything in the bracket.

(e) $(100g)^{\frac{1}{2}} = \sqrt{100}\, g^{\frac{1}{2}}$ .... ☞ Because 100 is in the brackets, we must take
$\qquad = \sqrt{100} \times \sqrt{g}$ the square root of 100 as well.
$\qquad = 10\sqrt{g}$ .... ☞ This is $10 \times \sqrt{g}$, not the tenth root of g.

(f) $25e^{\frac{1}{2}} = 25 \times e^{\frac{1}{2}}$ .... ☞ Only e is raised to the half power.
$\qquad = 25 \times \sqrt{e}$
$\qquad = 25\sqrt{e}$ You might not need to write all these steps in
getting the answer.

4. Write in index form:

(a) $\sqrt[4]{a^3} = a^{\frac{3}{4}}$ .... ☞ Using the rule $\sqrt[n]{x^m} = x^{\frac{m}{n}}$.

(b) $\sqrt[3]{y^4} = y^{\frac{4}{3}}$ $\qquad$ (c) $\sqrt{x^7} = x^{\frac{7}{2}}$

(d) $(\sqrt[3]{p})^8 = p^{\frac{8}{3}}$ $\qquad$ (e) $(\sqrt{w})^5 = w^{\frac{5}{2}}$ $\qquad$ (f) $(\sqrt[5]{mn})^2 = (mn)^{\frac{2}{5}}$

5. Write without fractional indices:

(a) $d^{\frac{3}{2}} = \sqrt{d^3}$ .... ☞ Using the rule $x^{\frac{m}{n}} = \sqrt[n]{x^m}$.

(b) $x^{\frac{4}{5}} = \sqrt[5]{x^4}$ $\qquad$ (c) $(yz)^{\frac{5}{6}} = (\sqrt[6]{yz})^5$

(d) $(4a)^{\frac{1}{2}} = \sqrt{4a}$ $\qquad$ (e) $(27e)^{\frac{1}{3}} = \sqrt[3]{27e}$ $\qquad$ (f) $(16m)^{\frac{3}{4}} = (\sqrt[4]{16m})^3$
$\qquad\quad = \sqrt{4} \times \sqrt{a}$ $\qquad\qquad\quad = \sqrt[3]{27} \times \sqrt[3]{e}$ $\qquad\qquad\quad = (\sqrt[4]{16})^3 \times (\sqrt[4]{m})^3$
$\qquad\quad = 2\sqrt{a}$ $\qquad\qquad\quad = 3\sqrt[3]{e}$ $\qquad\qquad\quad = 8\sqrt[4]{m^3}$

6. Given $x = 25$, $y = 27$ and $z = 16$, find:

(a) $x^{\frac{1}{2}} = 25^{\frac{1}{2}}$ $\qquad$ (b) $z^{\frac{1}{4}} = 16^{\frac{1}{4}}$ $\qquad$ (c) $y^{\frac{2}{3}} = 27^{\frac{2}{3}}$
$\qquad\; = \sqrt{25}$ $\qquad\qquad = \sqrt[4]{16}$ $\qquad\qquad = (\sqrt[3]{27})^2$
$\qquad\; = 5$ $\qquad\qquad = 2$ $\qquad\qquad = 9$

7. Simplify:

(a) $(u^{16})^{\frac{1}{2}} = u^8$ .... ☞ Multiply the indices.

(b) $(n^8)^{\frac{3}{4}} = n^6$ .... ☞ $8 \times \dfrac{3}{4} = 6$

(c) $(9a^6)^{\frac{1}{2}} = 3a^3$ .... ☞ 9 is also raised to the half. $9^{\frac{1}{2}} = \sqrt{9} = 3$

(d) $2m^{\frac{1}{2}} \times 3m^{\frac{1}{2}} = 6m^1$ .... ☞ Multiply the numbers, add the indices.
$\qquad\qquad\qquad = 6m$ $m^1 = m$. We don't need to write the one.

(e) $20h^{\frac{3}{4}} \div 4h^{\frac{1}{2}} = 5h^{\frac{1}{4}}$ .... ☞ Divide the numbers, subtract the indices.
$\qquad\qquad\qquad = 5\sqrt[4]{h}$ You could leave the answer in index form.

$$x^2 \div x^3 = x^{-1} \quad \text{by the index rules}$$

$$\text{but} \quad x^2 \div x^3 = \frac{x^2}{x^3}$$

$$= \frac{1}{x}$$

The question is the same so the answer must be the same.

$$x^{-1} = \frac{1}{x}$$

and

$$x^{-m} = \frac{1}{x^m}$$

Example:
Write in fractional form:

(a) m^{-1} **(b)** a^{-5} **(c)** e^{-2} **(d)** $(5t)^{-1}$ **(e)** $2x^{-1}$ **(f)** $7k^{-4}$ **(g)** $(3h)^{-2}$ **(h)** pq^{-3}

Solution:

(a) $m^{-1} = \dfrac{1}{m}$ (b) $a^{-5} = \dfrac{1}{a^5}$ (c) $e^{-2} = \dfrac{1}{e^2}$ (d) $(5t)^{-1} = \dfrac{1}{5t}$

(e) $2x^{-1} = 2 \times \dfrac{1}{x}$ (f) $7k^{-4} = 7 \times \dfrac{1}{k^4}$ (g) $(3h)^{-2} = \dfrac{1}{(3h)^2}$ (h) $pq^{-3} = \dfrac{p}{q^3}$

$\quad = \dfrac{2}{x}$ $\quad = \dfrac{7}{k^4}$ $\quad = \dfrac{1}{9h^2}$

Example:
Write in index form: **(a)** $\dfrac{1}{g}$ **(b)** $\dfrac{1}{n^7}$ **(c)** $\dfrac{2}{y^4}$ **(d)** $\dfrac{5}{z}$ **(e)** $\dfrac{1}{4t}$ **(f)** $\dfrac{a^3}{b^3}$

Solution:

(a) $\dfrac{1}{g} = g^{-1}$ (b) $\dfrac{1}{n^7} = n^{-7}$ (c) $\dfrac{2}{y^4} = 2y^{-4}$

(d) $\dfrac{5}{z} = 5z^{-1}$ (e) $\dfrac{1}{4t} = (4t)^{-1}$ (f) $\dfrac{a^3}{b^3} = a^3 b^{-3}$

We can now combine our negative and fractional indices.

$$x^{-1} = \frac{1}{x} \quad \text{and} \quad x^{\frac{1}{2}} = \sqrt{x} \quad \text{so} \quad x^{-\frac{1}{2}} = \frac{1}{\sqrt{x}}$$

Example:
Change from index form: **(a)** $e^{-\frac{1}{2}}$ **(b)** $y^{-\frac{1}{3}}$ **(c)** $2m^{-\frac{1}{2}}$ **(d)** $7t^{-\frac{1}{4}}$ **(e)** $(9y)^{-\frac{1}{2}}$ **(f)** $(8p)^{-\frac{2}{3}}$

Solution:

(a) $e^{-\frac{1}{2}} = \dfrac{1}{\sqrt{e}}$ (b) $y^{-\frac{1}{3}} = \dfrac{1}{\sqrt[3]{y}}$ (c) $2m^{-\frac{1}{2}} = 2 \times \dfrac{1}{\sqrt{m}}$

$\quad = \dfrac{2}{\sqrt{m}}$

(d) $7t^{-\frac{1}{4}} = 7 \times \dfrac{1}{\sqrt[4]{t}}$ (e) $(9y)^{-\frac{1}{2}} = \dfrac{1}{\sqrt{9y}}$ (f) $(8p)^{-\frac{2}{3}} = \dfrac{1}{(\sqrt[3]{8p})^2}$

$\quad = \dfrac{7}{\sqrt[4]{t}}$ $\quad = \dfrac{1}{3\sqrt{y}}$ $\quad = \dfrac{1}{4\sqrt[3]{p^2}}$

Example:
Write in index form: **(a)** $\dfrac{1}{\sqrt{k}}$ **(b)** $\dfrac{1}{\sqrt[6]{n}}$ **(c)** $\dfrac{3}{\sqrt{q}}$ **(d)** $\dfrac{1}{\sqrt{5w}}$ **(e)** $\dfrac{1}{\sqrt{z^3}}$ **(f)** $\dfrac{8}{\sqrt[3]{c^4}}$

Solution:

(a) $\dfrac{1}{\sqrt{k}} = k^{-\frac{1}{2}}$ (b) $\dfrac{1}{\sqrt[6]{n}} = n^{-\frac{1}{6}}$ (c) $\dfrac{3}{\sqrt{q}} = 3 \times \dfrac{1}{\sqrt{q}}$

$\quad = 3q^{-\frac{1}{2}}$

(d) $\dfrac{1}{\sqrt{5w}} = (5w)^{-\frac{1}{2}}$ (e) $\dfrac{1}{\sqrt{z^3}} = z^{-\frac{3}{2}}$ (f) $\dfrac{8}{\sqrt[3]{c^4}} = 8c^{-\frac{4}{3}}$

1. **Write in fractional form:**

   (a) h^{-1} = _____
   (b) t^{-3} = _____
   (c) e^{-7} = _____

   (d) $(3p)^{-1}$ = _____
   (e) $(6x)^{-2}$ = _____
   (f) $5a^{-1}$ = _____

   = _____
   = _____
   = _____

   (g) $8b^{-5}$ = _____
   (h) $(pq)^{-3}$ = _____
   (i) ab^{-4} = _____

2. **Write in index form:**

   (a) $\dfrac{1}{u}$ = _____
   (b) $\dfrac{1}{a^4}$ = _____
   (c) $\dfrac{1}{x^9}$ = _____

   (d) $\dfrac{4}{y}$ = _____
   (e) $\dfrac{7}{e^5}$ = _____
   (f) $\dfrac{1}{6k}$ = _____

   (g) $\dfrac{1}{(2n)^3}$ = _____
   (h) $\dfrac{a}{b^7}$ = _____
   (i) $\dfrac{p^2}{q^2}$ = _____

3. **Change from index form:**

   (a) $n^{-\frac{1}{2}}$ = _____
   (b) $a^{-\frac{1}{5}}$ = _____
   (c) $t^{-\frac{2}{3}}$ = _____

   (d) $u^{-\frac{3}{5}}$ = _____
   (e) $r^{-\frac{4}{3}}$ = _____
   (f) $w^{-\frac{3}{2}}$ = _____

   (g) $3d^{-\frac{1}{2}}$ = _____
   (h) $5q^{-\frac{1}{4}}$ = _____
   (i) $8x^{-\frac{5}{3}}$ = _____

   (j) $(7t)^{-\frac{2}{5}}$ = _____
   (k) $(4h)^{-\frac{1}{2}}$ = _____
   (l) $(9b)^{-\frac{3}{2}}$ = _____

   = _____
   = _____
   = _____

4. **Write in index form:**

   (a) $\dfrac{1}{\sqrt{e}}$ = _____
   (b) $\dfrac{1}{\sqrt{p}}$ = _____
   (c) $\dfrac{1}{\sqrt[3]{m}}$ = _____

   (d) $\dfrac{1}{\sqrt[8]{u}}$ = _____
   (e) $\dfrac{1}{\sqrt[6]{y}}$ = _____
   (f) $\dfrac{1}{\sqrt{n^3}}$ = _____

   (g) $\dfrac{1}{\sqrt[4]{a^3}}$ = _____
   (h) $\dfrac{1}{\sqrt[5]{k^2}}$ = _____
   (i) $\dfrac{2}{\sqrt{d}}$ = _____

   (j) $\dfrac{1}{\sqrt{2g}}$ = _____
   (k) $\dfrac{5}{\sqrt[3]{h}}$ = _____
   (l) $\dfrac{7}{\sqrt{v^5}}$ = _____

5. **Express without indices, where possible:**

   (a) $x^{-1}y$ = _____
   (b) $a^{\frac{1}{2}}b^{-\frac{1}{2}}$ = _____
   (c) u^2v^{-3} = _____

   = _____
   = _____
   = _____

   (d) $(c^{-1}d^{-1})^{-1}$ = _____
   (e) $y^{-4}z^{-3}$ = _____
   (f) $(t^{-1})^{\frac{1}{2}}$ = _____

   = _____
   = _____
   = _____

1. Write in fractional form:

   (a) $h^{-1} = \dfrac{1}{h}$ ☞ Using the rule $x^{-1} = \dfrac{1}{x}$

   (b) $t^{-3} = \dfrac{1}{t^3}$ ☞ Using the rule $x^{-m} = \dfrac{1}{x^m}$

   (c) $e^{-7} = \dfrac{1}{e^7}$

   (d) $(3p)^{-1} = \dfrac{1}{3p}$ ☞ Everything in the brackets is to the power of -1.

   (e) $(6x)^{-2} = \dfrac{1}{(6x)^2}$

           $= \dfrac{1}{36x^2}$ ☞ $6^2 = 36$

   (f) $5a^{-1} = 5 \times \dfrac{1}{a}$ ☞ $5a^{-1}$ means $5 \times a^{-1}$

         $= \dfrac{5}{a}$

   (g) $8b^{-5} = \dfrac{8}{b^5}$ ☞ $8 \times \dfrac{1}{b^5}$

   (h) $(pq)^{-3} = \dfrac{1}{(pq)^3}$ ☞ or $\dfrac{1}{p^3q^3}$

   (i) $ab^{-4} = \dfrac{a}{b^4}$ ☞ $a \times \dfrac{1}{b^4}$

2. Write in index form:

   (a) $\dfrac{1}{u} = u^{-1}$ ☞ Using the rule $\dfrac{1}{x} = x^{-1}$.

   (b) $\dfrac{1}{a^4} = a^{-4}$

   (c) $\dfrac{1}{x^9} = x^{-9}$

   (d) $\dfrac{4}{y} = 4y^{-1}$ ☞ $4 \times \dfrac{1}{y}$

   (e) $\dfrac{7}{e^5} = 7e^{-5}$ ☞ $7 \times \dfrac{1}{e^5}$

   (f) $\dfrac{1}{6k} = (6k)^{-1}$ ☞ or $\dfrac{1}{6}k^{-1}$ or $\dfrac{k^{-1}}{6}$

   (g) $\dfrac{1}{(2n)^3} = (2n)^{-3}$

   (h) $\dfrac{a}{b^7} = ab^{-7}$

   (i) $\dfrac{p^2}{q^2} = p^2q^{-2}$

3. Change from index form:

   (a) $n^{-\frac{1}{2}} = \dfrac{1}{\sqrt{n}}$ ☞ Using the rule $x^{-\frac{1}{2}} = \dfrac{1}{\sqrt{x}}$

   (b) $a^{-\frac{1}{5}} = \dfrac{1}{\sqrt[5]{a}}$ ☞ Using the rule $x^{-\frac{m}{n}} = \dfrac{1}{\sqrt[n]{x^m}}$

   (c) $t^{-\frac{2}{3}} = \dfrac{1}{\sqrt[3]{t^2}}$

   (d) $u^{-\frac{3}{5}} = \dfrac{1}{\sqrt[5]{u^3}}$

   (e) $r^{-\frac{4}{3}} = \dfrac{1}{\sqrt[3]{r^4}}$

   (f) $w^{-\frac{3}{2}} = \dfrac{1}{\sqrt{w^3}}$

(g) $3d^{-\frac{1}{2}} = \dfrac{3}{\sqrt{d}}$

(h) $5q^{-\frac{1}{4}} = \dfrac{5}{\sqrt[4]{q}}$

(i) $8x^{-\frac{5}{3}} = \dfrac{8}{\sqrt[3]{x^5}}$

(j) $(7t)^{-\frac{2}{5}} = \dfrac{1}{(\sqrt[5]{7t})^2}$ ☞ or $\dfrac{1}{\sqrt[5]{49t^2}}$

(k) $(4h)^{-\frac{1}{2}} = \dfrac{1}{\sqrt{(4h)}}$

$\qquad = \dfrac{1}{2\sqrt{h}}$

(l) $(9b)^{-\frac{3}{2}} = \dfrac{1}{\sqrt{(9b)^3}}$

$\qquad = \dfrac{1}{27\sqrt{b^3}}$ ☞ $\sqrt{9} = 3, \quad 3^3 = 27$

4. Write in index form:

(a) $\dfrac{1}{\sqrt{e}} = e^{-\frac{1}{2}}$ ☞ Using the rule $\dfrac{1}{\sqrt{x}} = x^{-\frac{1}{2}}$

(b) $\dfrac{1}{\sqrt{p}} = p^{-\frac{1}{2}}$

(c) $\dfrac{1}{\sqrt[3]{m}} = m^{-\frac{1}{3}}$

(d) $\dfrac{1}{\sqrt[8]{u}} = u^{-\frac{1}{8}}$

(e) $\dfrac{1}{\sqrt[6]{y}} = y^{-\frac{1}{6}}$

(f) $\dfrac{1}{\sqrt{n^3}} = n^{-\frac{3}{2}}$ ☞ Using the rule $\dfrac{1}{\sqrt[n]{x^m}} = x^{-\frac{m}{n}}$

(g) $\dfrac{1}{\sqrt[4]{a^3}} = a^{-\frac{3}{4}}$

(h) $\dfrac{1}{\sqrt[5]{k^2}} = k^{-\frac{2}{5}}$

(i) $\dfrac{2}{\sqrt{d}} = 2d^{-\frac{1}{2}}$ ☞ $2 \times \dfrac{1}{\sqrt{d}} = 2 \times d^{-\frac{1}{2}}$

(j) $\dfrac{1}{\sqrt{2g}} = (2g)^{-\frac{1}{2}}$

(k) $\dfrac{5}{\sqrt[3]{h}} = 5h^{-\frac{1}{3}}$

(l) $\dfrac{7}{\sqrt{v^5}} = 7v^{-\frac{5}{2}}$

5. Express without indices, where possible:

(a) $x^{-1}y = \dfrac{1}{x} \times y$

$\qquad = \dfrac{y}{x}$ ☞ $\dfrac{1}{x} \times \dfrac{y}{1}$

(b) $a^{\frac{1}{2}}b^{-\frac{1}{2}} = \sqrt{a} \times \dfrac{1}{\sqrt{b}}$

$\qquad = \dfrac{\sqrt{a}}{\sqrt{b}}$

(c) $u^2v^{-3} = \dfrac{u^2}{v^3}$ ☞ $u^2 \times \dfrac{1}{v^3}$

(d) $(c^{-1}d^{-1})^{-1} = c^1d^1$ ☞ Using the index laws, multiplying

$\qquad = cd$ the indices.

(e) $y^{-4}z^{-3} = \dfrac{1}{y^4 z^3}$ ☞ $\dfrac{1}{y^4} \times \dfrac{1}{z^3}$

(f) $(t^{-1})^{\frac{1}{2}} = t^{-\frac{1}{2}}$ ☞ Multiplying the indices

$\qquad = \dfrac{1}{\sqrt{t}}$ $\sqrt{\dfrac{1}{t}}$ is the same thing.

> To add or subtract fractions we need a common denominator.
> We can always find a common denominator by multiplying the denominators together.

Example:
Find: (a) $\dfrac{3}{x+y} + \dfrac{4}{x-y}$ (b) $\dfrac{a}{a+b} - \dfrac{b}{a-b}$ (c) $\dfrac{x+6}{x+5} + \dfrac{x-2}{x-4}$

Solution:

(a) $\dfrac{3}{x+y} + \dfrac{4}{x-y} = \dfrac{3(x-y)}{(x+y)(x-y)} + \dfrac{4(x+y)}{(x+y)(x-y)}$

$= \dfrac{3x-3y}{x^2-y^2} + \dfrac{4x+4y}{x^2-y^2}$

$= \dfrac{7x+y}{x^2-y^2}$

(b) $\dfrac{a}{a+b} - \dfrac{b}{a-b} = \dfrac{a(a-b)}{(a+b)(a-b)} - \dfrac{b(a+b)}{(a+b)(a-b)}$

$= \dfrac{a^2-ab}{a^2-b^2} - \dfrac{ab+b^2}{a^2-b^2}$

$= \dfrac{a^2-2ab-b^2}{a^2-b^2}$

(c) $\dfrac{x+6}{x+5} + \dfrac{x-2}{x-4} = \dfrac{(x+6)(x-4)}{(x+5)(x-4)} + \dfrac{(x-2)(x+5)}{(x+5)(x-4)}$

$= \dfrac{x^2-4x+6x-24}{(x+5)(x-4)} + \dfrac{x^2+5x-2x-10}{(x+5)(x-4)}$

$= \dfrac{2x^2+5x-34}{(x+5)(x-4)}$

> It is not necessary to expand the denominator. Leaving it in factorised form helps if we need to cancel.

> Factorising helps us to find the lowest common multiple (LCM) of algebraic expressions. The LCM must include **all** the factors of each expression, but any common factors need not be repeated.

Example:
Find the LCM of: (a) $x^2+9x+20$ and x^2-16 (b) $x^2-7x+12$ and $x^2+2x-15$.

Solution:

(a) $x^2+9x+20 = (x+5)(x+4)$
$x^2-16 = (x+4)(x-4)$
The LCM is $(x+5)(x+4)(x-4)$.

(b) $x^2-7x+12 = (x-3)(x-4)$
$x^2+2x-15 = (x+5)(x-3)$
The LCM is $(x-3)(x-4)(x+5)$.

> The lowest common denominator will always be the lowest common multiple of the denominators.

Example:
Find: (a) $\dfrac{x+2}{x^2-x} + \dfrac{x-3}{x^2+x}$ (b) $\dfrac{1}{x^2+3x-4} + \dfrac{1}{x^2-7x+6}$

Solution:

(a) $\dfrac{x+2}{x^2-x} - \dfrac{x-3}{x^2+x} = \dfrac{x+2}{x(x-1)} - \dfrac{x-3}{x(x+1)}$

$= \dfrac{(x+2)(x+1)}{x(x-1)(x+1)} - \dfrac{(x-3)(x-1)}{x(x-1)(x+1)}$

$= \dfrac{x^2+3x+2-(x^2-4x+3)}{x(x-1)(x+1)}$

$= \dfrac{7x-1}{x(x-1)(x+1)}$

(b) $\dfrac{1}{x^2+3x-4} + \dfrac{1}{x^2-7x+6} = \dfrac{1}{(x+4)(x-1)} + \dfrac{1}{(x-6)(x-1)}$

$= \dfrac{(x-6)+(x+4)}{(x+4)(x-1)(x-6)}$

$= \dfrac{2x-2}{(x+4)(x-1)(x-6)}$

$= \dfrac{2(x-1)^1}{(x+4)(x-1)(x-6)}$

$= \dfrac{2}{(x+4)(x-6)}$

1. Find:

(a) $\dfrac{1}{u} + \dfrac{1}{x}$ = _____

= _____

(b) $\dfrac{a}{b} - \dfrac{c}{d}$ = _____

= _____

(c) $\dfrac{2}{x+3} + \dfrac{3}{x+2}$ = _____

= _____

= _____

(d) $\dfrac{7x}{x+4} - \dfrac{2}{x-4}$ = _____

= _____

= _____

(e) $\dfrac{a+3}{a-2} + \dfrac{a+1}{a-1}$ = _____

= _____

= _____

(f) $\dfrac{m-5}{m} - \dfrac{m}{m-5}$ = _____

= _____

= _____

2. Find the lowest common multiple of:

(a) $x^2 - 9x$ and $x^2 - 81$

(b) $x^2 - 5x - 14$ and $(x-7)^2$

(c) $x^2 - x - 12$ and $x^2 - 6x + 8$

(d) $x^2 + 12x + 35$ and $x^2 - 2x - 35$

3. Find:

(a) $\dfrac{1}{x^2+9x+20} - \dfrac{1}{x^2+10x+24}$

(b) $\dfrac{x+3}{x^2+2x} + \dfrac{x-4}{x^2-2x}$

1. Find:

(a) $\dfrac{1}{u} + \dfrac{1}{x} = \dfrac{x}{ux} + \dfrac{u}{ux}$ ☞ The common denominator is the product ux.

$= \dfrac{x + u}{ux}$ ☞ When we have a common denominator, we simply add the numerators.

(b) $\dfrac{a}{b} - \dfrac{c}{d} = \dfrac{ad}{bd} - \dfrac{bc}{bd}$

$= \dfrac{ad - bc}{bd}$

(c) $\dfrac{2}{x+3} + \dfrac{3}{x+2} = \dfrac{2(x+2)}{(x+3)(x+2)} + \dfrac{3(x+3)}{(x+3)(x+2)}$ ☞ First get a common denominator.

$= \dfrac{2x+4}{(x+3)(x+2)} + \dfrac{3x+9}{(x+3)(x+2)}$ ☞ Expand the numerators.

$= \dfrac{5x+13}{(x+3)(x+2)}$ ☞ Add the numerators, collecting like terms.

(d) $\dfrac{7x}{x+4} - \dfrac{2}{x-4} = \dfrac{7x(x-4)}{(x+4)(x-4)} - \dfrac{2(x+4)}{(x+4)(x-4)}$ ☞ The denominator could also be written as $x^2 - 16$, but there is no need to expand.

$= \dfrac{7x^2 - 28x}{(x+4)(x-4)} - \dfrac{2x+8}{(x+4)(x-4)}$

$= \dfrac{7x^2 - 30x - 8}{(x+4)(x-4)}$ ☞ Be careful to subtract every term of the second fraction.

(e) $\dfrac{a+3}{a-2} + \dfrac{a+1}{a-1} = \dfrac{(a+3)(a-1)}{(a-2)(a-1)} + \dfrac{(a+1)(a-2)}{(a-2)(a-1)}$

$= \dfrac{a^2 - a + 3a - 3}{(a-2)(a-1)} + \dfrac{a^2 - 2a + a - 2}{(a-2)(a-1)}$ ☞ Expanding the numerators. There is no need to expand the denominator.

$= \dfrac{a^2 + 2a - 3}{(a-2)(a-1)} + \dfrac{a^2 - a - 2}{(a-2)(a-1)}$

$= \dfrac{2a^2 + a - 5}{(a-2)(a-1)}$ ☞ $\dfrac{2a^2 + a - 5}{a^2 - 3a + 2}$ is the same thing.

(f) $\dfrac{m-5}{m} - \dfrac{m}{m-5} = \dfrac{(m-5)^2}{m(m-5)} - \dfrac{m^2}{m(m-5)}$

$= \dfrac{m^2 - 10m + 25}{m(m-5)} - \dfrac{m^2}{m(m-5)}$

$= \dfrac{-10m + 25}{m(m-5)}$ ☞ We can leave the answer like this;

$= \dfrac{-5(2m-5)}{m(m-5)}$ or factorise the numerator.

2. Find the lowest common multiple of:

   (a) $x^2 - 9x$ and $x^2 - 81$
   $x^2 - 9x = x(x - 9)$ .... ☞ Common factor.
   $x^2 - 81 = (x + 9)(x - 9)$ .... ☞ Difference of two squares.
   Lowest common multiple is $x(x - 9)(x + 9)$. .... ☞ LCM includes all factors of both expressions.

   (b) $x^2 - 5x - 14$ and $(x - 7)^2$
   $x^2 - 5x - 14 = (x + 2)(x - 7)$
   $(x - 7)^2 = (x - 7)(x - 7)$
   LCM is $(x + 2)(x - 7)^2$ .... ☞ *All* factors of both expressions must be included.

   (c) $x^2 - x - 12$ and $x^2 - 6x + 8$
   $x^2 - x - 12 = (x - 4)(x + 3)$
   $x^2 - 6x + 8 = (x - 4)(x - 2)$
   LCM is $(x - 4)(x + 3)(x - 2)$

   (d) $x^2 + 12x + 35$ and $x^2 - 2x - 35$
   $x^2 + 12x + 35 = (x + 7)(x + 5)$
   $x^2 - 2x - 35 = (x - 7)(x + 5)$
   LCM is $(x + 7)(x - 7)(x + 5)$ .... ☞ The factors can be listed in any order.

3. Find:

   (a) $\dfrac{1}{x^2 + 9x + 20} - \dfrac{1}{x^2 + 10x + 24}$

   $= \dfrac{1}{(x + 5)(x + 4)} - \dfrac{1}{(x + 6)(x + 4)}$ .... ☞ First factorise the denominators.

   $= \dfrac{x + 6}{(x + 5)(x + 4)(x + 6)} - \dfrac{x + 5}{(x + 6)(x + 4)(x + 6)}$ .... The common denominator is the LCM.

   $= \dfrac{x + 6 - x - 5}{(x + 5)(x + 4)(x + 6)}$ .... ☞ Be careful with the signs. All of the second fraction must be subtracted.

   $= \dfrac{1}{(x + 5)(x + 4)(x + 6)}$ .... ☞ Collecting like terms.

   (b) $\dfrac{x + 3}{x^2 + 2x} + \dfrac{x - 4}{x^2 - 2x} = \dfrac{x + 3}{x(x + 2)} + \dfrac{x - 4}{x(x - 2)}$ .... ☞ First factorise,

   $= \dfrac{(x + 3)(x - 2)}{x(x + 2)(x - 2)} + \dfrac{(x - 4)(x + 2)}{x(x + 2)(x - 2)}$ .... then get a common denominator.

   $= \dfrac{x^2 - 2x + 3x - 6}{x(x + 2)(x - 2)} + \dfrac{x^2 + 2x - 4x - 8}{x(x + 2)(x - 2)}$

   $= \dfrac{x^2 + x - 6}{x(x + 2)(x - 2)} + \dfrac{x^2 - 2x - 8}{x(x + 2)(x - 2)}$

   $= \dfrac{2x^2 - x - 14}{x(x + 2)(x - 2)}$

> When multiplying fractions, it is always easiest if we cancel first.
> With algebraic fractions, we might need to factorise first
> so that we can then cancel any common factors.

Example:

Find $\dfrac{x^2 - 3x}{x^2 - 3x - 10} \times \dfrac{x^2 + 5x + 6}{x^2 - 9}$

Solution:

$\dfrac{x^2 - 3x}{x^2 - 3x - 10} \times \dfrac{x^2 + 5x + 6}{x^2 - 9} = \dfrac{x(x - 3)}{(x - 5)(x + 2)} \times \dfrac{(x + 3)(x + 2)}{(x + 3)(x - 3)}$ Factorise each expression.

$= \dfrac{x\cancel{(x-3)}^{\,1}}{(x-5)\cancel{(x+2)}_{1}} \times \dfrac{\cancel{(x+3)}^{\,1}\cancel{(x+2)}^{\,1}}{\cancel{(x+3)}_{1}\cancel{(x-3)}_{1}}$ This has been repeated to show the cancelling.

$= \dfrac{x}{x - 5}$

> There is no need to expand the answer. It is quite acceptable to leave it in factorised form.

Example:

Find: **(a)** $\dfrac{x^2 - 16}{x^2 - 4x + 3} \times \dfrac{3x - 9}{x^2 + 4x}$ **(b)** $\dfrac{x^2 + 8x - 20}{x^2 + 8x + 15} \times \dfrac{x^2 - 5x - 14}{x^2 - 9x + 14}$

Solution:

(a) $\dfrac{x^2 - 16}{x^2 - 4x + 3} \times \dfrac{3x - 9}{x^2 + 4x} = \dfrac{(x+4)(x-4)}{\cancel{(x-3)}_{1}(x-1)} \times \dfrac{3\cancel{(x-3)}^{\,1}}{x\cancel{(x+4)}_{1}}$

$= \dfrac{3(x - 4)}{x(x - 1)}$

(b) $\dfrac{x^2 + 8x - 20}{x^2 + 8x + 15} \times \dfrac{x^2 - 5x - 14}{x^2 - 9x + 14} = \dfrac{(x+10)\cancel{(x-2)}^{\,1}}{(x+5)(x+3)} \times \dfrac{\cancel{(x-7)}^{\,1}(x+2)}{\cancel{(x-7)}_{1}\cancel{(x-2)}_{1}}$

$= \dfrac{(x+10)(x+2)}{(x+5)(x+3)}$

> *Remember*: To divide by a fraction, we multiply by its reciprocal.

Example:

Find: **(a)** $\dfrac{x^2 - 1}{x^2 + x} \div \dfrac{x^2 - 1}{x^2 - x}$ **(b)** $\dfrac{x^2 + 4x - 12}{x^2 - 36} \div \dfrac{x^2 - 8x + 12}{x^2}$

Solution:

(a) $\dfrac{x^2 - 1}{x^2 + x} \div \dfrac{x^2 + 1}{x^2 - x} = \dfrac{x^2 - 1}{x^2 + x} \times \dfrac{x^2 - x}{x^2 + 1}$

$= \dfrac{\cancel{(x+1)}^{\,1}(x-1)}{x\cancel{(x+1)}_{1}} \times \dfrac{x(x-1)}{x^2 + 1}$

$= \dfrac{(x - 1)^2}{x^2 + 1}$

(b) $\dfrac{x^2 + 4x - 12}{x^2 - 36} \div \dfrac{x^2 - 8x + 12}{x^2} = \dfrac{x^2 + 4x - 12}{x^2 - 36} \times \dfrac{x^2}{x^2 - 8x + 12}$

$= \dfrac{\cancel{(x+6)}^{\,1}\cancel{(x-2)}^{\,1}}{\cancel{(x+6)}_{1}(x-6)} \times \dfrac{x^2}{(x-6)\cancel{(x-2)}_{1}}$

$= \dfrac{x^2}{(x - 6)^2}$

1. Find:

(a) $\dfrac{4}{x^2-4} \times \dfrac{x+2}{2}$ = _____

= _____

= _____

(b) $\dfrac{c^2-36}{c+6} \times \dfrac{3}{3c-18}$ = _____

= _____

= _____

(c) $\dfrac{x+3}{x^2+5x+4} \times \dfrac{x+4}{x^2-4x-21}$ = _____

= _____

= _____

(d) $\dfrac{a^2-25}{a^2-5a} \times \dfrac{5a}{a+5}$ = _____

= _____

= _____

(e) $\dfrac{e^2+e-12}{e^2+3e-10} \times \dfrac{e^2+5e-14}{e^2+5e+4}$ = _____

= _____

= _____

(f) $\dfrac{u^2-6u-16}{u^2-16} \times \dfrac{u^2-4u}{u^2-4}$ = _____

= _____

= _____

2. Find:

(a) $\dfrac{x+8}{3} \div \dfrac{2x+16}{4}$ = _____

= _____

= _____

(b) $\dfrac{r^2}{r^2-7r} \div 2r$ = _____

= _____

= _____

(c) $\dfrac{n^2+2}{n^2-2n} \div \dfrac{n-2}{n^2+2n}$ = _____

= _____

= _____

(d) $\dfrac{s}{s^2+5s+6} \div \dfrac{s^2+2s}{s^2+s-6}$ = _____

= _____

(e) $\dfrac{z^2-3z}{z^2-9} \div \dfrac{z^2-8z-9}{z^2}$

= _____

= _____

= _____

(f) $\dfrac{m^2+7m+12}{m^2+11m+18} \div \dfrac{m^2+9m+18}{m^2+8m+12}$

= _____

= _____

= _____

ALGEBRAIC FRACTIONS—MULTIPLYING AND DIVIDING Worked Solutions

1. Find:

(a) $\dfrac{4}{x^2-4} \times \dfrac{x+2}{2} = \dfrac{4}{(x+2)(x-2)} \times \dfrac{x+2}{2}$ ☞ First factorise,

$= \dfrac{\cancel{4}^2}{\cancel{(x+2)}(x-2)_1} \times \dfrac{\cancel{x+2}^1}{\cancel{2}_1}$ then cancel. (This step has been repeated just to show the cancelling. You don't need to write it twice.)

$= \dfrac{2}{x-2}$ ☞ Multiply the numerators and multiply the denominators.

(b) $\dfrac{c^2-36}{c+6} \times \dfrac{3}{3c-18} = \dfrac{(c+6)(c-6)}{c+6} \times \dfrac{3}{3(c-6)}$ ☞ First factorise,

$= \dfrac{\cancel{(c+6)}\cancel{(c-6)}^1}{\cancel{c+6}_1} \times \dfrac{\cancel{3}^1}{\cancel{3(c-6)}_1}$ then cancel.

$= 1$ ☞ Multiply the numerators and denominators. The answer is 1 (not zero).

(c) $\dfrac{x+3}{x^2+5x+4} \times \dfrac{x+4}{x^2-4x-21}$

$= \dfrac{x+3}{(x+4)(x+1)} \times \dfrac{x+4}{(x-7)(x+3)}$ ☞ Always factorise first.

$= \dfrac{\cancel{x+3}^1}{\cancel{(x+4)}(x+1)_1} \times \dfrac{\cancel{x+4}^1}{(x-7)\cancel{(x+3)}_1}$ ☞ Cancel.

$= \dfrac{1}{(x+1)(x-7)}$ ☞ There is no need to expand. Leave the answer in factorised form. [The answer is not $(x+1)(x-7)$. There must be a 1 in the numerator.]

(d) $\dfrac{a^2-25}{a^2-5a} \times \dfrac{5a}{a+5} = \dfrac{(a+5)(a-5)}{a(a-5)} \times \dfrac{5a}{a+5}$

$= \dfrac{\cancel{(a+5)}^1\cancel{(a-5)}^1}{\cancel{a}\cancel{(a-5)}_1} \times \dfrac{5\cancel{a}^1}{\cancel{a+5}_1}$

$= 5$ ☞ $\dfrac{5}{1}$ is the same thing, but we don't write the 1.

(e) $\dfrac{e^2+e-12}{e^2+3e-10} \times \dfrac{e^2+5e-14}{e^2+5e+4}$

$= \dfrac{\cancel{(e+4)}^1(e-3)}{(e+5)\cancel{(e-2)}_1} \times \dfrac{(e+7)\cancel{(e-2)}^1}{\cancel{(e+4)}_1(e+1)}$

$= \dfrac{(e-3)(e+7)}{(e+5)(e+1)}$ ☞ or $\dfrac{e^2+4e-21}{e^2+6e+5}$

(f) $\dfrac{u^2-6u-16}{u^2-16} \times \dfrac{u^2-4u}{u^2-4}$

$= \dfrac{(u-8)\cancel{(u+2)}^1}{(u+4)\cancel{(u-4)}_1} \times \dfrac{u\cancel{(u-4)}^1}{\cancel{(u+2)}_1(u-2)}$

$= \dfrac{u(u-8)}{(u+4)(u-2)}$ ☞ There is no need to expand.

2. Find:

(a) $\dfrac{x+8}{3} \div \dfrac{2x+16}{4} = \dfrac{x+8}{3} \times \dfrac{4}{2x+16}$ ☞ To divide by a fraction, we multiply by its reciprocal.

$= \dfrac{x+8}{3} \times \dfrac{4}{2(x+8)}$ ☞ Factorise.

$= \dfrac{\cancel{x+8}^{\,1}}{3} \times \dfrac{\cancel{4}^{\,2}}{2\cancel{(x+8)}_{\,1}}$ ☞ Cancel.

$= \dfrac{2}{3}$

(b) $\dfrac{r^2}{r^2-7r} \div 2r = \dfrac{r^2}{r^2-7r} \times \dfrac{1}{2r}$ ☞ The reciprocal of $2r$ is $\dfrac{1}{2r}$.

$= \dfrac{\cancel{r^2}^{\,1}}{_1\,\cancel{r}(r-7)} \times \dfrac{1}{2\cancel{r}\,_1}$ ☞ Factorise, then cancel.

$= \dfrac{1}{2(r-7)}$ ☞ $\dfrac{1}{2r-14}$ is the same thing but we usually leave the answer in factorised form.

(c) $\dfrac{n+2}{n^2-2n} \div \dfrac{n-2}{n^2+2n} = \dfrac{n+2}{n^2-2n} \times \dfrac{n+2n}{n-2}$

$= \dfrac{n+2}{n(n-2)} \times \dfrac{n(n+2)}{n-2}$

$= \dfrac{n+2}{_1\,\cancel{n}(n-2)} \times \dfrac{\cancel{n}^{\,1}(n+2)}{n-2}$

$= \dfrac{(n+2)^2}{(n-2)^2}$ ☞ This cannot be simplified.

(d) $\dfrac{s}{s^2+5s+6} \div \dfrac{s^2+2s}{s^2+s-6}$

$= \dfrac{s}{s^2+5s+6} \times \dfrac{s^2+s-6}{s^2+2s}$

$= \dfrac{\cancel{s}^{\,1}}{_1\,(s+3)(s+2)} \times \dfrac{^1\,(s+3)(s-2)}{_1\,\cancel{s}(s+2)}$

$= \dfrac{s-2}{(s+2)^2}$

(e) $\dfrac{z^2-3z}{z^2-9} \div \dfrac{z^2-8z-9}{z^2}$

$= \dfrac{z^2-3z}{z^2-9} \times \dfrac{z^2}{z^2-8z-9}$

$= \dfrac{z(z-3)^{\,1}}{(z+3)(z-3)\,_1} \times \dfrac{z^2}{(z-9)(z+1)}$

$= \dfrac{z^3}{(z+3)(z-9)(z+1)}$

(f) $\dfrac{m^2+7m+12}{m^2+11m+18} \div \dfrac{m^2-9m+18}{m^2+8m+12}$

$= \dfrac{m^2+7m+12}{m^2+11m+18} \times \dfrac{m^2+8m+12}{m^2+9m+18}$

$= \dfrac{(m+4)(m+3)^{\,1}}{(m+9)(m+2)\,_1} \times \dfrac{^1\,(m+6)(m+2)}{(m+6)(m+3)\,_1}$

$= \dfrac{m+4}{m+9}$

Algebra	A branch of maths that uses symbols.
Algebraic expression	Any term, or combination of terms, using pronumerals.
Base	(In indices) the number, or term, that is multiplied. (In 5^2, 5 is the base).
Binomial	An expression which is the sum, or difference, of two terms.
Binomial product	The multiplication of binomials.
Coefficient	A number in front of a pronumeral. In $5x^3 + 9x^2 - 7x + 1$, the coefficient of x^3 is 5, the coefficient of x^2 is 9 and the coefficient of x is -7.
Collecting like terms	Adding or subtracting terms.
Common denominator	Of fractions, a number divisible by all the denominators. (12 is the lowest common denominator of $\frac{1}{4}$ and $\frac{5}{6}$).
Common factors	Divide evenly into all the given numbers. For example, 3 is a common factor of 9 and 12.
Completing the square	Adding a number or term to an expression to make it a perfect square.
Consecutive numbers	Numbers that follow one another in order (like 11, 12, 13, 14).
Cross method	A method used to factorise harder trinomials, involving a cross.
Denominator	The bottom part of a fraction. (For the fraction $\frac{2}{3}$, 3 is the denominator.)
Difference of two squares	A special binomial product. One square minus another square.
Distributive law	The law that says, for example, $2 \times (4 + 7) = 2 \times 4 + 2 \times 7$.
Elimination	Getting rid of. In simultaneous equations, removing one of the pronumerals.
Equation	An algebraic expression that includes an '=' sign.
Expand	To write out in longer form.
Factor	A number (or term) that divides into another. (7 is a factor of 21.)
Factorising	Writing something as a product of its factors. (The opposite of expanding.)
Formula	A rule using pronumerals. (For example, $A = \pi r^2$ is the formula for the area of a circle).
Function (of x)	A rule using a pronumeral (x). (Replacing x with a number gives a value of the function.)
$f(x)$	A function of x. We say 'f of x'.
Generalised arithmetic	Using algebraic expressions for questions, without knowing any numbers.
Grouping symbols	Commonly called brackets; (parentheses), [brackets] and {braces}.
Highest common factor	The largest number that divides into all the given numbers.
Index	The number of times something is multiplied by itself. (3^4, 4 is the index.)
Index notation	Written using indices.
Indices	The plural of index. (1 index, 2 or more indices.)
Inequality	Something unequal. For example, $6 > 4$, $-a \le -1$, $8 \ne 0$.
Inequation	An expression involving an inequality sign. For example, $3x + 1 > 7$.
LCM	Lowest common multiple.

Like terms	Terms that have exactly the same pronumeral part.
Lowest common multiple	The smallest number, or term, that is a multiple of all the given numbers, or terms.
Number line	A line with integers (whole numbers) marked along it in order.
Numeral	A number.
Numerator	The top part of a fraction. (For the fraction $\frac{2}{3}$, 2 is the numerator.)
Operations	Addition, subtraction, multiplication and division.
Plotting	Placing on a grid or a number line.
Power	Another name for an index.
Product	The result of a multiplication.
Pronumeral	A symbol that stands instead of a number.
Quadratic	Involving expressions with squares.
Quadratic equation	An equation involving a term that is squared.
Quadratic formula	A formula used to give the solution of a quadratic equation.
Reciprocals	Multiply to give 1. ($\frac{3}{2}$ is the reciprocal of $\frac{2}{3}$.)
Satisfies	Makes a statement true. ($x = 2$ satisfies $x + 1 = 3$.)
Simplify	Make simpler, usually by adding, subtracting, etc.
Simultaneous	Occurring at the same time.
Simultaneous equations	Two, or more, equations involving the same pronumerals, whose solution satisfies both equations at the same time.
Solution	The answer to an equation, or to a problem.
Square	A number, or term, multiplied by itself.
Subject	The pronumeral before the equals sign in a formula. (In $E = mc^2$, E is the subject.)
Substitution	Replacing a pronumeral with a number.
Sum by difference	A binomial product where one binomial is the sum of 2 terms and the other is the difference of the same 2 terms.
Surd	A square root of a number that is not a perfect square. ($\sqrt{2}$ and $\sqrt{3}$ are surds, $\sqrt{4}$ is not, because $\sqrt{4} = 2$.)
Table of values	Values obeying a given rule, placed in a table.
Term	Each of the members of an algebraic expression, for example, $2x$, $8y^2$, 7, $9ab$.
Trinomial	An expression with three terms.
Unlike terms	Terms whose pronumeral parts are not exactly the same.